THE SCIENCE OF THE GOLF SWING

Dr David Williams

First published in Great Britain in 1969

Copyright © David Williams (now asserted by Mr David Michael Snyder – grandson)

DAVID WILLIAMS, D Sc., F.I.Mech.E., F.R.Ae.S., C.Eng.
Formerly Deputy Chief Scientific Officer at the Royal Aircraft Establishment, Farnborough

Editing, design and typesetting by UK Book Publishing
www.ukbookpublishing.com

Published by Luke Porter in conjunction with UK Book Publishing
luke@thescienceofthegolfswing.com

ISBN: 978-1-916572-05-8

THE SCIENCE OF THE GOLF SWING

Fig 1. The well-known multiflash photograph of Bobby Jones swinging a driver

The same image is used in the Appendix document

Reproduced by kind permission Yale University Art Gallery

Purchased with a gift from Philip Bronstein, B.S. 2012, in honor of

David Swensen, Ph.D. 1980, Hon. 2014

© Harold Edgerton/Palm Press, Inc.

To the memory of that prince of sportsmen, Lord Brabazon of Tara, PC, GBE, MC, whose views on the game of golf I found a never-failing source of stimulation

CONTENTS

FOREWORD TO "THE SCIENCE OF THE GOLF SWING" 2023 EDITION

Mick Snyder (grandson of Dr David Williams)

My grandfather David Williams was an engineer with a distinguished career as detailed in the biography given at the back of the book.

Writing as the only surviving relative who knew him, here are a few words on my memories of the man, his passions and his character.

Born on 4 August 1894 his start in life was in a poor family, his father being a local stonemason. But there were some interesting characters around him - his grandmother read the Financial Times, and his uncle was a maths teacher.

He was the oldest of three brothers who were brought up in Cwmsychbant, a hamlet in mid Wales comprising, at that time, half a dozen houses, a couple of farms, a chapel and a tiny shop. His siblings were John, an optician, and the FRS-awarded physicist Evan James "Desin" Williams who played a major role during WWII in developing countermeasures against the German U-boats.

His primary school was in the nearby village of Llanwenog, although his native tongue was Welsh, he and his fellow pupils were not allowed to use it inside the school grounds - under threat of being beaten. Luckily such times are well past.

After leaving school he took the civil service entrance exam and passed with high marks which led to work at Customs and Excise in South Shields. There he found the work crashingly boring, frustrating and totally unstimulating however his chance to leave soon came - it was 1914 and he joined the Army to fight in northern France in the First World War.

He had met his wife-to-be at a local fair in 1912. Sarah Emily Jones was the daughter of a very rich local aristocratic family living in a mansion in Llanllwni. They were married despite their greatly different social backgrounds - where the two sets of parents refused to talk to each other - in 1914. Their marriage was stronger than any of the social pressures and continued rock solid until my grandfather's death in 1970.

I remember him as a ferociously argumentative family-loving man with infectious enthusiasm for his many interests ranging from astronomy to photography to sport to motor cars, and most of all his work.

Stories about him abound. He lived for his work – he was known to go to work on a Bank Holiday and only finding out that it was one by being told so by the guard at the locked gates of the Royal Aircraft Establishment. Another time - during WWII - he was speaking in Welsh on the phone to his brother Desin who was working in a senior scientific role for the war office. Minutes after his call ended, Military Police knocked on his door and wanted to know why he had been speaking in a "foreign" language - the switchboard operator had overheard the call and had assumed that the callers were up to no good...

This, his second book, The Science of the Golf Swing, was inspired by his love of golf. There were many opinions at the time of where the power of the swing came from, most of which, according to him, were "utter rubbish" (he wasn't a man to hide his true feelings...), but he couldn't, much to his frustration at that time, actually prove it.

However, years earlier he had seen the multi-flash photo of the golf swing of Bobby Jones, the famous American golfer, and he bought a little book of the individual photos where, by flicking the pages, you saw a moving picture of the swing. He realised that these were the core material for him to do a detailed mathematical analysis - which led to a scientific paper and the idea for this book. This original piece of work (included in this book) resulted in reappraisal and debunking of many accepted, but entirely wrong, conceptions of how the swing works.

ORIGINAL PREFACE

S ome two years ago, being very interested in the golf swing and not a little intrigued by the multiplicity of conflicting opinions ventilated in the golfing press on what precisely takes place in a golf swing as executed by a top-class player, I decided to make a mathematical study of the problem. The result of this study was that for the first time in the history of the game a full understanding of the flail-like action of the swing was obtained. That is to say, the problem of what forces are applied to the club and how the club reacts to those forces in a properly executed golf swing was completely solved. A full account of the mathematical analysis involved was published in an article in the 'Quarterly Journal of Mechanics and Applied Mathematics' for June 1967 - a scientific periodical with a world-wide circulation.

The conclusions recorded in that article were of such outstanding interest to the average player that I thought it worthwhile bringing them to his notice - hence this book, in which the fruits of the mathematical study are presented to him in an easily digestible form.

In writing it I have tried to bear in mind that, however interested the ordinary golfer may be in new facts about the mechanics of the swing, he is still more interested in knowing how those facts can be used to help him achieve a better and more powerful swing. In this I have every hope that he will not be disappointed. For I am firmly convinced that players who fail to make progress at golf owe their failure not so much to their own lack of aptitude but to poor instruction leading to wrong conception of the swing. The reason why present-day golf instruction is less than adequate is not because the instructors themselves lack prowess at the game but because, well as they play it themselves, they are hide-bound by false ideas, as anybody who reads this book will discover.

Other important aspects of golf besides the golf swing find a place here but for the moment enough said.

CHAPTER I

INTRODUCTORY REMARKS

When, as a scientist and research engineer, I embarked a couple of years ago on the project of investigating the mystery - for mystery it has been over the years of the golf swing, I realised that the problem is two-fold. The first part, which must be solved before the second part can be tackled, is to find out what forces must be applied to the club to make it take up the sequence of positions which go to make up a properly executed downswing.

The second part of the problem is to obtain a clear understanding of the way a first-class player moves his body so that his hands can generate the required force with the least effort.

As the club is an inanimate object, which is made to move from its position at the top of the swing to its position at impact by a force applied (by the hands) at the grip end of the shaft, the first part of the problem is amenable to mathematical analysis. Its solution -the first ever presented as far as I know - was published in a paper of mine to the Quarterly Journal of Mechanics and Applied Mathematics (June 1967) - a scientific periodical with a world-wide circulation.

The second part of the problem - what body movements the player must carry out so as to enable his hands to apply the force which the above-mentioned solution shows to be necessary cannot be treated mathematically. This however, does not mean that it cannot be treated rationally, for the main requirement for its successful treatment is already available in the form of the known force applied by the hands.

Before the dynamical problem of the swing was solved mathematically in the scientific paper referred to above, teachers of the game were reduced to guessing at the force transmitted by the hands to the club. As these guesses were wildly off target, it is no wonder that ideas about the relative contributions of different parts of the body to the production of clubhead speed have proved to be somewhat in error. Indeed, to this day one cannot open a golf book or periodical without reading the most fantastic nonsense about the golf swing.

Two of the objectives aimed at in this book stand out from the rest. The first is to give the reader a clear understanding of the force applied to the club by the hands in the downswing as executed by a first-class player.

The second is to explain, partly by reference to simple line drawings copied from film sequences of well-known players, and partly by means of simple experiments which the reader can carry out for himself, the movements made by different parts of the body during the swing and the way they contribute to the end product - the pull exerted by the hands on the clubshaft.

In pursuing this second objective I have adopted a course which I have not seen followed in any golf book that I have read. This is to concentrate attention on certain key movements which go to make up the complete swing, in other words to dissect the swing into its individual parts.

One of the greatest mistakes in my view that golf teachers make is to try and teach the swing as a whole to an adult learner. It works for a young pupil if he has any aptitude, because the young have a very strong imitative faculty. They have also a good physical memory, so that when at last after a period of trial and error their action suddenly falls into the right groove they seldom forget it again, so that in the end the right action becomes instinctive. Not however, with the late learner who, even after stumbling on the right approach, is likely to lose it again and never to recover it. For him indeed the process of trial and error can be long and frustrating as well as fruitless. The quickest and most painless method for him is to understand and become familiar with certain key movements in the swing. Understanding such movements does not of course enable him to incorporate them into his swing all at once. Their integration into the swing as a whole necessarily takes time. The great advantage of this kind of approach, however, over the trial and error method is that the learner knows what he is trying to do and is not for ever blundering from one error to another without any clear objective in sight.

The situation as between learning the fundamentals of the game at an early age and learning them later in life is paralleled by the experience of learning a foreign language. Young children pick up a foreign language without any trouble. They soak it up accent, grammar and all, from hearing it spoken by those around them. By contrast the adult's progress is painfully slow - the hurdles of grammar, vocabulary, accent and idioms have all to be laboriously learnt before any sort of competence can be reached. The adult golfing addict is in a parallel position. However often he watches tournament golfers, little of what he sees soaks in. The very ease with which the professionals perform - the art with which they conceal their art - makes it that much more difficult for him to penetrate their disguise and get at some of the fundamentals that lie behind it.

That is why the golf swing needs to be dissected into its component parts and why the significance of each part must be separately understood if the adult learner is to make real progress. A main objective of this book is to do just that. There are, however, other matters discussed in this book which should be of real interest to all golfers whether rabbits or tigers. And not only to players but to manufacturers also. For it is amply demonstrated in a later chapter that their ideas concerning the qualities that clubs ought to have simply cannot bear scientific examination. But of that more anon.

CHAPTER II

HOW THE MATHEMATICAL APPROACH SOLVES THE PROBLEM OF THE GOLF SWING

It is necessary to say a few words here on what is meant when it is said that the dynamical problem of the golf swing has been mathematically solved.

The first step towards a solution is to choose an actual recorded swing whose classical correctness is universally accepted. Certain basic features of this swing are then taken as corner-stones in the mathematical analysis, which builds up the whole motion from the top of the swing to the point of impact. The correctness of the solution is finally checked by comparing the mathematically derived swing with the recorded swing at *every instant throughout the motion*. If at all instants the two swings are identical, the correctness of the derived swing is proved beyond a shadow of doubt. Once such an identity has been established, one can say with certainty that the same forces must have been applied to the club in the two cases.

This means that we now have in the mathematically derived swing a key to the forces that must have been applied in the photographically recorded swing. It means that for the very first time in the history of the game we have positive evidence of what a top-class player does to a golf club at every moment throughout a classically executed downswing. We know whether he used any wrist leverage and, if so, at what part of the swing he did use it. We know whether there is such a thing as delaying the hit. We know how and where the real power that spells distance is applied and we know - to the pound - the magnitude of the forces applied by the hands throughout the swing. Many other things can be deduced from the mathematically derived swing that would otherwise remain a mystery to be interpreted by different players according to their fancy.

I mentioned above that the first step towards the mathematical solution was to choose a swing of classical correctness for which a complete record exists. In the well-known multiflash photograph of Bobby Jones swinging a driver we have just what is required – a classical swing with a photographic record which shows the position of hands and club at intervals of 1/100 sec. from start to finish - some thirty-three separate exposures. This is shown in the frontispiece which originally taken by Messrs A. G. Spalding Bros. Inc. by whose kind permission it is here reproduced.

The particular features of this photograph that I have taken as corner-stones in the mathematical analysis are the following:

(i) The first stage of the downswing consists of a one-piece movement of shoulders, arms, wrists and clubshaft, which brings the left arm into a horizontal position and the club to a point behind, and in line with, the head.

(ii) The time for this one-piece movement must agree with the recorded time. Equally the time taken to cover the remainder of the swing, which brings the clubhead from behind the head to the point of impact, must also be identical with the recorded time. The recorded time is of course measured by the number of exposures between the two positions, each interval between successive exposures clocking 1/100 second.

(iii) The clubhead speed at the end of the first, one-piece stage, and at impact must agree with that recorded. This speed is easily measured since the size of the ball in the photograph is known and can be used as a yardstick for measuring the distance between the two last pictures of the clubhead before impact.

The mathematically derived swing that satisfies these conditions is shown in Fig. 2 and the correctness of the solution may now be gauged by comparing this swing with that recorded in the multiflash photograph of Fig. 1. In the derived swing of Fig. 2 the hands move in a circular arc from the top of swing at A to the bottom at C, with the centre of rotation at O. Simultaneously the clubshaft moves from its initial position AD to its impact position CL. The one-piece first stage takes the hands from A to B and the clubshaft from AD to BE, with no change in wrist-cock, i.e. in the angle between arm and clubshaft. This means that the clubhead traces out a circular arc just like the hands but of greater radius.

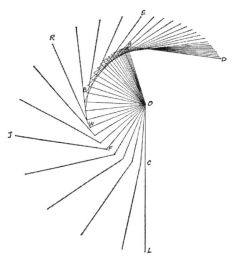

Fig. 2. The mathematically derived swing – to be compared
with the actual swing seen in the Frontispiece

In the second stage, during which the hands move from B to C, the angle between arm and clubshaft - the cocking angle - no longer remains fixed but starts to open out until at impact arm OC and clubshaft CL are in line.

There are many things of great interest to be learnt about this swing and these will be considered in detail in the next chapters. What I would like the reader to do at this point is to compare the relative positions of hands and clubshaft in the derived swing as depicted in Fig. 2 with those in the multiflash picture of Fig 1, particularly over the second stage of the swing. The most convenient way of doing this is to start at the impact point and examine the relative positions of hands and clubshaft at successive exposures, counting backwards from that point. For example, one sees that at the 5th exposure, i.e. 4/100 sec. before impact, the clubshaft has not quite reached the horizontal in the derived swing. Comparison with the photograph shows the clubshaft to be in an identical position. At 4/100 sec. earlier in the swing (9th exposure from impact) one notices that the shaft has just passed the vertical on its way down in Fig. 2, again identical with the position it has reached in the photograph at the same moment. But there is no need to make further comparisons here, for the reader can see for himself the remarkable agreement between the calculated swing and the photographic record.

Once having established that the derived swing of Fig. 2 correctly represents the recorded swing of Fig. 1, we have the key to the true interaction between player and club when Bobby Jones was photographed swinging a driver. That key lies in the mathematical analysis from which the swing shown in Fig. 2 was calculated. It was essential to calculate that swing, because the only way to prove that the mathematics was correct was to demonstrate that the swing calculated from it was identical with the actual swing of Bobby Jones as recorded in the multiflash photograph of Fig.1. With that accomplished, no one can call in question the many interesting and instructive conclusions that flow from the mathematical analysis, and it is my business in this book to present those conclusions in everyday language which every golfer can understand.

CHAPTER III

FIRST, OR ONE-PIECE, STAGE
OF THE DOWNSWING

As already explained, an essential characteristic of the downswing is that it consists of two distinct stages. The first is a one-piece motion with shoulders, arms, hands *and* club moving as if frozen together, and all rotating about the same centre with the same angular velocity and acceleration. This merges into the second stage of the motion, where *the shoulders and arms continue to move solidly together in one piece* but the connection between hands and clubshaft becomes unfrozen to allow the wrists to start uncocking to accommodate the outward swing of the shaft.

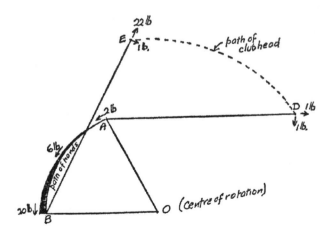

Fig. 3. One-piece first stage of downswing – Pull of hands represented by thickness of shaded band. Note the very small drag force (1 lb.), perpendicular to the shaft – the only force requiring the use of hand leverage

12

Fig. 3 reproduces the first or one-piece stage of the motion already shown in Fig. 2, where it extends from A to B for the hands and from D to E for the clubhead. It is enough here to show the initial position OAD and the final position OBE of the arms and clubshaft. A word of explanation is necessary here. I have referred to what connects the hands to the centre of rotation as the 'arms', but this is not of course strictly true since the centre of rotation is midway between the shoulders. Thus OA and OB in Fig. 3 are made up of arms *and* shoulders.

All I want to show on this figure are the forces involved - the drag forces at the clubhead and the pull which the hands have to apply to overcome them. Let us look first at the drag forces at the clubhead. These are divided into two component parts, a force in the direction of the shaft and acting along it and so tending only to stretch it, and a force at right angles to the shaft tending to bend it. The force at right angles to the shaft is only 1lb. at the start D and *remains the same all the way* to E, when the first stage of the downswing is completed. The slight bending thus caused in the shaft - seen clearly in the photograph of Fig. 1 - is resisted by the cocked wrists which do not start uncocking throughout the first stage.

The force *along* the shaft, on the contrary, gradually increases from its initial value of 1 lb. at D to 22 lb. at E. The hands resist this force by acting as the rim of a wheel of which the shoulders form the hub and the arms the spokes. The rotating shoulders (hub), actuated by the hips, force the arms (spokes) round and so enable the hands (rim) to apply the necessary pull along their arc of travel. This pull starts at only 2 lb. at A and then grows in the way *shown by the thickness of the shaded band* to 6 lb. halfway along and to 20 lb. at the completion of the first stage.

Importance of the rate at which the pull of the hands grows

As mentioned above the thickness of the shaded band is a measure of the pull of the hands at each point along their arc of travel AB. For example, its thickness halfway along is less than a third of that at the end B and represents a pull of only 6 lb. compared with 20 lb. at B. To put it another, the pull increases by only 4 lb. (from 2 lb. to 6 lb.) over the first half of the arc but increases by 14 lb. (from 6 lb. to 20 lb.) over the second half. This increase in the rate of growth as the hands move along their arc is of the essence of a correct swing and is of cardinal importance. It is the only way in which to maintain the steady drag of 1 lb. at the clubhead and so keep a steady cocking pressure at the wrists, which is the sure safeguard against premature uncocking.

You may wonder what would happen if, instead of the pull with the hands growing in the way illustrated in Fig. 3 (i.e. growing very slowly over the first half of the arc AB but rapidly quickening its rate of growth over the second half) it grew more steadily, i.e. with about the same growth rate over the whole arc. The mathematics shows clearly what would happen - a much heavier (wrist-cocking) pressure on the wrists over the first half of the arc followed immediately by an equally heavy negative (uncocking) pressure over the second half. The player can cope with the initial extra pressure on his wrists but when that pressure is immediately released and actually reversed nothing can stop the involuntary uncocking of the wrists. Such premature uncocking means ruin to the swing, because it allows the clubhead to swing out instead of following its close orbit round the body. This premature transit to a wider orbit slows down the hands and involves an expenditure of effort that should be reserved for the second stage of the swing.

It cannot be too strongly emphasised that it is in this first stage of the downswing that the average player's swing goes astray. If he manages to negotiate it correctly he will be in a favourable position for negotiating the second stage. But the temptation to go wrong is very strong. Have another look at Fig. 3, where you see that at the starting point A the pull is only 2 lb. and even halfway along the arc is only 6 lb. Yet this is the start of a swing that is going to send the ball some 260 yards. Pulls like 2 lb. and 6 lb. are chicken-feed even to the average golfer. He could more than double these figures with ease and, unfortunately for him,

14

that is just what he does do, with the consequences already described.

The dual problem of starting the downswing both one-piece and with crescendo acceleration is discussed in more detail later on. To end this chapter, I would call the reader's attention again to the two most significant conclusions which have emerged from the mathematical analysis. They are:

(a) The very light pull (2 lb.) which the hands apply to the club at the very start and the gradually increasing rate with which it grows into a 20 lb. pull at the end of the first stage.

(b) The remarkable fact that what the hands do is to apply force along the shaft but next to no leverage.

Regarding conclusion (a) I would like to refer the reader to Bobby Jones's chapter on 'Timing and rhythm' in his book 'Golf is my game'*. There he quotes something written by Harold Hilton in 1903 concerning a long driver of that era – a certain S Mure Fergusson. What particularly distinguished Fergusson's swing according to Hilton was that he not only took up the club in a leisurely and deliberate fashion on the upswing but that *he maintained the same leisurely method at the beginning of the downswing*. The operative words according to Jones *I have italicised*. For he makes the point that the well known injunction 'slow back' is not enough, since plenty of players can restrain their impetuosity during the upswing but few have the self-control to maintain that restraint during the start of the downswing.

---

*   *Chatto and Windus (1961)*

CHAPTER IV

SECOND STAGE OF THE DOWNSWING

We now come to the second stage of the downswing where the really serious muscular effort has to be put in by the player. Referring to Fig. 2 again, you will note that the first, or one- piece, stage ends when the hands have reached position B and the clubhead position E. Hands and shaft during that stage accelerate in concentric circular arcs, the hands along the arc AB and the clubhead along the arc DE. Up to the point B the hands are accelerating and in the case of Bobby Jones's swing their speed is about 34 ft/sec. when they reach that point, the clubhead meanwhile having accelerated from nothing at D to about 50 ft/sec. at E.

At this point a radical change takes place. The hands (with arms and shoulders moving solidly together in one piece) gain no more speed but keep up their 34 ft/sec. all the way from B to their position at impact C. Not so, however, the clubhead. For although the grip end of the shaft moves at 34 ft/sec. with the hands, the head, because of swinging out to a wider orbit, rapidly gains speed until at impact it is moving at 165 ft/sec. (113 m.p.h.) But this is no more than can be deduced directly from the photograph of Fig. 1.

The real interest lies in the way the pull of the hands and the inertia drag forces at the clubhead grow as the hands move from B to C along their arc of travel. This is best shown by a separate diagram (Fig. 4) which includes both stages of the swing. There is no point in including all the relative positions of hands and clubshaft shown in Fig. 2. Five positions alone of hands and clubshaft are therefore shown in Fig. 4 - at the start of the first stage OAD, at the end of the first stage OBE, at the end of the second stage (impact position) OCL and at two intermediate positions in the second stage, OWR and OFJ. The pull exerted by the hands however is represented continuously all along their arc of travel from A to C by the shaded band whose thickness at any position of the hands is a measure of the pull they exert in that position. The shaded band for the arc AB has already been shown in Fig. 3 and discussed in the last chapter. It shows the pull of the hands growing at a rapidly increasing rate from 2 lb. at A to 20 lb. at B. It can be seen from Fig. 4 that the pull goes on increasing in the second stage to reach a maximum of 70 lb. when the hands are at F. It has only dropped to 50 lb. when the hands are within a foot of their position at impact. In that foot however the pull drops from 58 lb. to nothing. For at impact the velocity of the clubhead is a maximum which means that the acceleration is zero, which means that the force causing acceleration is zero also.

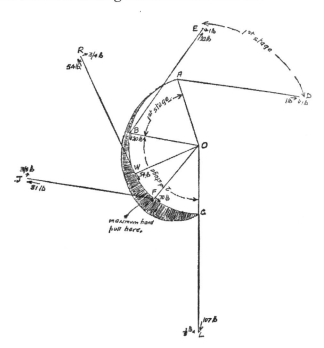

Fig. 4. First and second stages of downswing. Thickness of shaded band is measure of hands pull at each point on arc of travel

Of equal interest is to see the way the inertia drag forces at the clubhead behave as the downswing proceeds. In each of the five positions shown both the drag along the shaft and the drag at right angles to the shaft are shown. They are highly illuminating.

The drag along the shaft starts at 1 lb., reaches 22 lb. at the end of the first stage (position E), 54 lb. at R, 81 lb. at J and 107 at L. However, it is the smallness of the drag at right angles to the shaft that is most striking -1 lb. throughout the first stage (from D to E), 3/4 lb. at R, 3/8 lb. at J and 1/8 lb. at L, in other words negligibly small. The special interest lies in the fact that only the drag force at right angles to the shaft has to be countered by a levering action of the wrists and that over the whole of the second stage this is of absolutely no account. At point F for example, where it is popularly supposed that power is poured into the stroke by wrist leverage, the force at the clubhead at right angles to the shaft causing this leverage is only 6 ounces!

The mathematics therefore proves beyond any argument that hand (or wrist-uncocking) leverage has nothing to do with accelerating the clubhead in what is usually referred to as the 'hitting area'. This is of course contrary to the teaching of the great majority of the professional pundits.

A word of explanation is perhaps desirable here to prevent any chance of misunderstanding by the reader. In the above paragraphs I referred first to the pull which the hands exert in their direction of travel, i.e. along ABC. It is this pull alone that concerns the player because it is only the work performed by this pull that produces clubhead speed. I referred secondly to the pull which the drag of the clubhead applies *along the shaft*, which is a different matter. You can see from Fig. 4 that only when the hands are at point W is the drag of the head along WR (i.e. 54 lb.) in line with the pull of the hands tangential to the arc, which for balance must also be 54 lb. When, however, the hands have reached point F the 81 lb. inertia drag of the head is no longer in line with the pull of the hands of 70 lb. along the tangent to their arc of travel. The explanation of course is that the 81 lb. drag is balanced not by the pull of

70 lb. along the arc alone but by a combination of this 70 lb. and a pull of 40 lb. along FO. This latter pull merely puts the arm in tension and does nothing to increase clubhead speed, but of course must be there for balance.

At impact the whole of the inertia drag of the clubhead is taken by this useless stretching of the left arm when the useful pull along the arc has dropped to zero.

Since, according to what I have said above, hand leverage is negligibly small, you may ask what in that case snaps the clubhead from J to L (Fig. 4) in just 1/25 second. Centrifugal force is the answer, as the mathematics makes abundantly clear.

Incidentally, the fact that no hand leverage action is applied to the club in the later stages of the swing can be deduced without the help of mathematics. There are plenty of action photographs taken at practically instantaneous exposures (so cutting out distortion due to camera shutter effects) of crack players at late positions in the swing. None of them shows any sign of appreciable bending of the shaft by hand leverage. The forward bend shown in Fig. 1 is proved in Chapter XII to be due to another cause. Now take your driver and bend it by pressing its head against the floor. You find you can bend it into quite a pronounced bow without any trouble and can cause a very distinct bend in it with only a slight hand leverage. Why then bother about strengthening the hands? This simple experiment is enough by itself to prove to anyone capable of independent thought that where a shaft remains straight in an action photograph it is because of absence of any leverage tending to bend it. Yet the wrong idea persists even among the top names in the world of golf. Such wrong notions may not affect their own game, because their practice has little connection with their theories. The pity is, though, that they disseminate these misleading ideas to their pupils who, unlike their teachers, try to marry their practice to theories they are taught.

Not that abandonment of certain wrong ideas would not benefit the professionals themselves. They might well save themselves for example the time and trouble, now expended on strengthening the hands, for more worthwhile objectives.

It is interesting to speculate on the cause of the widespread belief that the hands possess a store of pent-up energy in their cocked position ready for release when they uncock as the point of impact is approached. It is almost certain that the belief is due to the fact that the hands, sensing the powerful action of the force in making the shaft catch up with them, naturally uncock in sympathy. This uncocking of the hands, natural though it may feel, is caused entirely by the centrifugal force acting on the clubhead and not by any direct muscular action of the wrists. The fact that the two actions occur simultaneously is what causes the player to accept the false and ignore the true origin of the power that snaps the clubhead into line with the hands at impact. As well might the motorist credit the muscular power of his foot with the powerful action of servo brakes!

How the heavy hand-pulls in the 'hitting area' are generated.

Anyone looking at the way the pull of the hands build up in the later part of the second stage might well be surprised at its magnitude. After all, a pull of 70 lb. when the hands are as low down as the point F in Fig. 4, and therefore hardly in an advantageous position for exerting a pull along their arc of travel, may well be thought to be surprisingly large. It would indeed be surprisingly large if it were a steady pull. What makes it possible is that it is not a static but a dynamic pull. In other words it is less a pull than a shock. The action is of the same nature as a multitude of other actions met with in everyday life. If a door is to be broken down it is useless putting a shoulder to it and applying a steady push. The only hope is to apply shock tactics and take a run at it. A closer analogy perhaps is the reaper's technique with the reaping hook. The first stage of the forward stroke is devoted to building up the speed of his blade - gaining kinetic energy - so that it can barge its way through when it meets the resistance of the swathe.

In Fig. 2, what has to be realised is that, although the arc AB covered in the first stage is much shorter than the arc BC covered in the second stage it takes twice the time. However, it is only when one looks at the times taken in relation to distances covered by the clubhead that the shock-tactics, characteristic of the golf swing, can be properly appreciated. To cover the arc DE (Figs. 2 and 4) of the first stage the clubhead takes 24/100 of a second, but it takes only a further 12/100 to cover the arc ERJL nearly four times longer than arc DE. In Fig. 4, as already explained, the thickness of the shaded band is a measure of the pull exerted by the hands at any point in their arc of travel. The area of the shaded band between any two positions on the arc is a measure of the contribution to clubhead speed made between any two positions of the hands. On this basis one can see at a glance that the shaded area over the first-stage arc AB is only 1/10 of the total shaded area, which means that 9/10 of the total effort must be applied over second-stage arc BC. If we think in terms of the time taken, this means that after 2/3 of the total downswing time only 1/10 of the total effort has been expended and therefore 90% of the total effort has to be packed into the remaining 1/3 of the time.

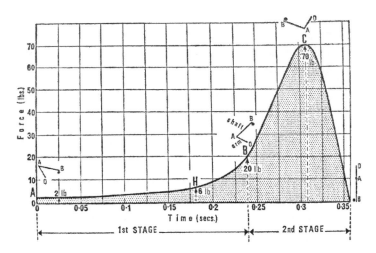

Fig. 5. How pull of hands along their arc of travel

varies during downswing on a time basis

The diagram of Fig. 5 makes very clear how late in the downswing the real power is applied. In this diagram the time taken from the moment of starting the downswing is marked along the base and the height of the curve shows how the pull exerted by the hands (marked at the left of the diagram) grows as the time passes. Point B on the curve marks the end of the first stage when 0.24 sec. out of the total 0.36 sec. has already elapsed and the pull has reach 20 lb. Look, however, at the way the hand pull peaks up to 70 lb. in the next 0.06 sec. and then just as suddenly drops to nothing.

I have drawn this diagram for the special purpose of emphasising the shock nature of the pull which the hands exert. Incidentally the position of the arm and clubshaft is shown at three points in time - at the start A, at the end of the first stage B and at C where the maximum pull occurs.

Lessons to be learnt from the shock character of the hands pull.

Much is to be learnt from the above demonstration of the shock resistance met with in the final stage of the golf swing. The first lesson it teaches is that the one-piece first stage (from A to B in Fig. 5) is no more than an insignificant prelude to the second stage so far as the expenditure of muscular effort and the gaining of clubhead speed is concerned. Its function is rather to provide a running start for overcoming the heavy resistance which the hands meet in the later stages of the swing.

You will remember my saying earlier on that the hands gain speed only up to the end of the first stage (point B in Fig. 4) but thereafter in the second stage do no more than maintain that speed. And when you look at the curve of Fig. 5 (and the suddenly mounting resistance in the second stage) you can readily understand why it is as much as the hands can do to maintain their speed, despite the running start they get.

Although the pull of the hands in the first stage is of little account compared with what follows in the second stage, it must be remembered, as I emphasised in the previous chapter, that the way the pull grows in the first stage is of vital importance to the success of the second stage. Unless it grows in the way indicated by the curve AHB (Fig. 5) the second stage will be ruined, because the hands due to premature uncocking will never have the chance of exerting their heavy pull in the second stage. Note how slowly the pull grows from 2 lb. at the start A to 6 lb. at the half-time point H and then how rapidly it grows as the end B of the first stage is approached.

So here is the second lesson taught by the growth (of pull) curve of Fig. 5 - that it is essential to start the pull gently if the shock resistance met with in the second stage is to be overcome. This is not easy, for there is unquestionably an almost irresistible temptation to switch on full power right from the word go.

Since the shock resistance is met with late in the swing it behoves the player to get his muscular apparatus lined up in good time to deal with it. The sudden hip-shift (discussed later) at the top of the swing is an essential part of this lining up.

Such questions as how to remove the temptation to switch on full power right from the start of the downswing and what the body has to do in order to ensure a correct start and an efficient application of power in the second stage of the swing are discussed in the next chapters.

In concluding this chapter I must get the reader to fully understand two points.

1st point is to understand the way centrifugal force operates in accelerating the clubhead in the later stages of the downswing. Look at OWR in Fig. 4. The centrifugal force at the clubhead R pulls it away from the centre of rotation O. It is like a giant's hand pulling the clubhead R and the centre O apart, so straightening out the angle OWR between arm and shaft until the two finally snap into line at impact.

2nd point is to appreciate the magnitude of that pull between O and R. It is some 19 lb. in position OWR. Of this 12 lb. acts perpendicular to the shaft and it is this that urges the head to accelerate round the hands and not hand leverage. Indeed a 12 lb. force applied to the head by hand leverage would *bend the shaft 12 inches out of straight* – enough to break the shaft!

CHAPTER V

How the new scientific approach cuts through the tangled undergrowth of traditional ideas and leads to a better understanding of the swing and so to better performance

In the light of the previous chapters we now have, for the first time in the history of the game, full knowledge of what a top class player does to the club at every instant throughout the downswing. And since whatever he does to it is done with his hands, this is as much as to say that we know exactly what his hands do throughout the swing. We know that, except in the initial stage of the downswing, his hands apply no leverage to the club but only a plain pull directed along the shaft. In other words, that in the second stage, where nine-tenths of the real work is done, the clubhead might just as well be connected to the hands by a piece of string. Thus it is the business of the shoulders - themselves actuated by the hips - to transmit the requisite pull via the arms and hands to that 'string'.

What I propose to do here is to examine, in the light of action photographs of top-class players and of the newly gained knowledge of what the hands have to do, the way the main source of muscular power finds its outlet at the hands. A few exercises are also described which are designed to give you direct experience of the 'feel' associated with certain key movements of the swing. As a first step in this direction I want to explain the kind of flail action that is used in the golf swing.

The swing as a two-link flail action.

It will be useful first to discuss flail action in general with a view to showing that the golf swing is the simplest, though far from the most natural, of all the flail actions used by man for multiplying the velocity of the implements he handles. This makes it possible then to demonstrate the practical bearing which that all important fact has on the average player's swing. It is hardly necessary to define flail action, as most people have heard of the ancient method of threshing corn by using two stout sticks connected together by a leather thong. Grasping one of the sticks by its end, thresher lets the other stick hang behind his back and then slings it overhead to land full length flat on the corn. The leather hinge makes it impossible to apply leverage to the second or 'business' stick, which is therefore subjected throughout the operation to a force directed *only along its length*. The action is exactly analogous to that between the arms and the clubshaft in the golf swing where the hands act as hinges and the pull is directly along the shaft. The whole action depends on centrifugal force which 'swishes' the second stick round the first with velocity multiplied several fold.

The flail action used by the thresher, however, is far from simple, for his hands are themselves part of another flail consisting of shoulders, upper arms and forearms. Yet, despite this complicated combination of flails and the nicety of timing it involves, the thresher experiences little difficulty in landing the business end of his flail just where he wants to. The reason, of course, is that the action is largely a natural one. Action from shoulders to leather hinge is instinctive, identical as it is with the wielding of an axe or beating something with a heavy stick. The thresher is therefore able to concentrate his attention on timing the action of the final link of the flail - the business end.

The way flail action enters into various familiar activities may help to highlight the essential simplicity of the particular type used in the golf swing. But first I would ask you to carry out a few simple exercises which you can perform without leaving your armchair. Place your right elbow E on the chair arm AA as indicated diagrammatically in Fig. 6(a). *With elbow (and shoulders) fixed* raise your hand H as shown. Suppose now you want to smack the chair hard without moving the elbow. Your hand H traverses the circular arc HH, meeting the chair at H. Note that there is *no flail action here* because centrifugal force, although acting on the hand, gets no chance to do useful work because it is directed along the forearm EH, merely trying to stretch it.

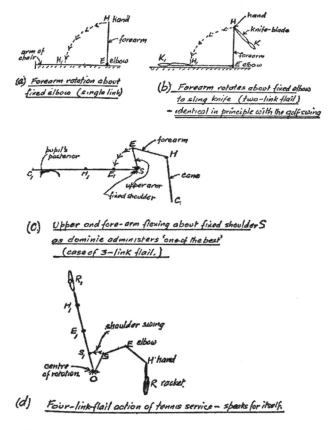

Fig 6. *Two-, three- and four-link flail actions illustrated*

Next, with the elbow and shoulder still fixed and the hand raised as before, hold a table knife by its blade between finger and thumb and let it hang down in the position shown in Fig 6. (b). As the hand now moves along its arc HH, it can sling the knife handle K to land on the chair arm at K, with real force. This is *genuine flail action* because the motion of the hand allows centrifugal force to whip the knife handle with multiplied velocity as the (cocking) angle EHK opens out into the straight line EHK at impact. This two-link flail action is the simplest of all flail actions. It represents in principle exactly what takes place in an orthodox golf swing, but more of that later.

Meanwhile, consider what happens when a further link is added to the flail by freeing the hitherto fixed elbow while the shoulder S still remains fixed as in Fig 6. (c). This is the well-remembered technique favoured by headmasters for administering 'six of the best'. The three links of the flail straighten out in the way illustrated at the moment of impact between the cane and the victim's posterior. It is a more complicated action than the two-link-flail action shown in Fig 6. (b), but it is such a natural action that it comes easy to the most non-athletic type of schoolmaster.

A still more effective way of 'laying into' the stroke would be to draw back the shoulder S in the backswing, but only the more sadistically minded dominie would resort to this and, even so, with doubtful success, as some nicety of timing would be involved!

The extra link introduced by the moving shoulder S and the consequent much increased power is, however, just what is needed in the service action at tennis and this is illustrated in Fig. 6(d), which is a four-link-flail action that speaks for itself.

Complicated as this four-link-flail action looks, there is no real difficulty in timing it. And why? It is because the whole action is a natural one. If the racket is replaced by a cricket ball, the three link flail thus formed is that used for the most natural of all actions - learnt in the nursery and no doubt familiar to pre-historic man - throwing a stone.

There is an interesting and instructive experiment I would like you to do at this stage because you will find it very illuminating. In doing the knife-slinging exercise of Fig. 6(b) you will remember that you were holding the tip of the table knife between forefinger and thumb and that you found it an easy and natural action to sling the handle against the chair arm. I want you to repeat that action and note this time at what stage the blade starts sliding between finger and thumb. Note, in other words, when the uncocking action starts. You will find that the cocking angle EHK remains unchanged for the first part of the arc HH, which your hand traverses, which means that forearm and knife start off one piece, just like the first half of the golf downswing. The purpose, of course, is to build up enough centrifugal force in the knife handle to spontaneously fling it into its outer orbit while the hands complete their arc of travel. I want you to note particularly how lightly you held the blade tip during the one-piece first stage, i.e. how little leverage you had to apply with finger and thumb to start the action and prevent the knife-handle from lagging behind.

A further point of the utmost significance in this exercise is the fact that it provides *positive proof that what whips the knife handle forward in the final stage of the stroke is centrifugal force and not any leverage applied to the blade.* In fact the centrifugal force here has to overcome not only the inertia of the handle but also the frictional drag applied by the pressure exerted on the blade by the finger and thumb. Strange how this simple exercise is enough to demolish a belief, still stubbornly held by some, that it is hand leverage that whips the clubhead at the ball in what is called the 'hitting area'!

Take next something a good deal longer, though no heavier, than the table knife - say 4 or 5 times the length of the knife. A light stick or cane will do admirably. Try now repeating the simple two-link-flail action of Fig. 6(b) with the longer implement. If you hold the cane lightly like the knife blade, you will have to go slow to prevent the stick slipping and lagging behind. As a result, centrifugal force builds up too late to apply any slinging action before the hands reach the end of their arc. You have therefore to help it by gripping more firmly to enable you to apply stronger leverage with the fingers early on, so as to build up speed quickly enough for centrifugal force to do its job in time.

The fact is that increasing the length of the second link of the flail makes it less responsive to the slinging action of centrifugal force *no matter how light it is*. That is why the second, or swinging, member of the thresher's flail must not exceed a certain proportion of the length of the first member or it *becomes unmanageable independently of the second member's weight*. However light it is, if it is too long in relation to the first member, the thresher will not be able to land it flat on the corn for it will persist in lagging behind. This is why there is a definite limit to the length of a clubshaft as the mathematics brings out very clearly.

This is a useful lesson to learn, for it demonstrates the fact that if the second link of a flail is more than about 1.5 times the length of the first, excessive leverage has to be applied at the start of the action so as to generate speed quickly enough for centrifugal force to do its stuff in time.

Of course, lengthening the second link of the flail has a similar effect to shortening the first link. Thus shortening the forearm EH in Fig. 6(b) upsets the timing in the same way as lengthening the knife EK. In the golf swing the first link is the radius of the arc traversed by the hands. This is reduced by any appreciable bending of the arms and results in reduced clubhead speed and faulty timing. Hence the desirability of a straight left arm throughout. This question will be discussed in more detail later.

The main purpose of the above disquisition on flail action is to emphasise the fact that the golf swing represents the simplest of all flail actions - *the two-link flail of* Fig. 6(b).

That the golf swing is no more than a two-link flail action is proved by the fact that the mathematically derived swing of Fig.2, which faithfully represents Bobby Jones's swing (as recorded in the photograph of Fig. 1) depends on there being only two links - one joining the hands to the centre of rotation and the other, i.e. the clubshaft, joining the hands to the clubhead. It is therefore at first sight surprising that the golf swing, despite its basic simplicity, is so full of snags. At first sight it certainly is rather odd but only at first sight.

There is a very good reason why the golf swing is troublesome to learn, and why it is particularly troublesome for those who take up golf in middle age or those who turn to golf from other ball games. It is the instinctive - the almost invincible urge - to make the swing a three-link-flail or even a four-link-flail action right at the start of the backswing *if the arms are allowed to move independently of the shoulders*. For then, instead of the hands being connected to the centre of rotation by a single-link structure of shoulders and arms moving as one piece, they are connected by a two-link structure, the shoulders constituting one link and the arms the other. If, in addition, the left arm is bent at the elbow the action becomes a four-link-flail action, the correct timing of which offers insuperable difficulties.

In the light of the above remarks it is fair to say that nothing has emerged from the mathematical analysis of the golf swing of greater practical importance to the average player than the conclusion that the golf swing is essentially a two-link-flail action. It is, of course, the first link in the flail - the one-piece link of shoulders and arms which the player can do something about, for the second link, i.e. the clubshaft, cannot be other than one piece.

The idea of starting the upswing as well as the downswing as a one-piece movement of shoulders, arms and clubshaft is not new and has often been advocated. Little emphasis, however, has been placed on the fact that *shoulders and arms move in unison - a single link - right throughout the swing* and not just in the first stage of the upswing and downswing. It is an idea that drastically simplifies the golf swing and is bound to prove of real help to the average player. He will be gratified not only by its simplicity but by the increased reliability which it confers.

In the first stage of the upswing, just as in the first stage of the downswing, the second link of the flail - the clubshaft - moves in one-piece with the first link of shoulders and arms, so that *over these stages of the swing there is effectively only one link*. It is only when the left arm approaches the horizontal, both when going up and when coming down that the clubshaft becomes a separate link to form a two-link flail. This change occurs as the wrists start cocking about one-third the way up and start uncocking about a third of the way down.

The one-piece upswing

Emphasis was placed in the preceding paragraphs on the one-piece character of the shoulders-arms motion but nothing was said about the motion of the legs-hips unit. I use the word unit advisedly because the legs and hips move together as much in unison as the shoulders and arms. The point I now want to make is that *in the upswing* the superstructure of shoulders and arms is *directly geared* to the substructure of hips and legs. By this I mean that when the shoulders have turned through a full right-angle the hips, turning at half that rate, have turned through half a right-angle. They start together and reach their maximum turn together. There is, in other words, no question of the shoulders (and arms) starting the movement, with the hips (and legs) following after a split-second time-lag. Put still another way, there is no chain-reaction between the movements of the shoulder-arms unit and the hips-legs unit on the upswing as there is on the downswing.

Perhaps something ought to be said here about the concept of chain-reaction as applied to the golf swing. The idea it is supposed to convey is that the swing is made up of a series of movements, each one triggering off the next but with a split-second time-lag separating consecutive movements. This is the most poisonous idea that has ever been dangled before the unsuspicious learner. This chain-reaction idea is the one picture of the golf swing that should be avoided like the plague. There is a world of difference between a series of movements that are *geared* together and a series connected together by *chain-reaction*. In a motor car the engine is directly geared to the road wheels: the engine drives the gear-box shaft, which drives the prop shaft which drives the crown wheel, which drives the axle shafts, which drive the road wheels. There is no time-lag between the engine and the road wheels despite the series of intermediate movements. That is the situation in the golf upswing – legs, hips, shoulders and arms are geared together with no element lagging behind its neighbour.

What this means is that the moment you start the upswing the legs and hips begin to move and the weight begins to shift in time with the shoulders-arm unit. The bend of the left knee is a very different kind of movement from the rotation of the shoulders but it is directly geared to it, just as the reciprocating motion of the engine piston, though very different in kind from the rotational motion of the road wheels, is still directly geared to that rotational motion. Looking at action photographs of top-class players from the front, you could easily be led to believe that no leg movement takes places till the clubhead has covered a couple of feet. Views taken with the camera facing the target, however, show clearly that the left knee begins to bend right from the start.

This idea of all body elements being geared together in the upswing is not only correct, it is also by far the simplest conception and by far the easiest to time. Starting the shoulder turn while the legs and hips are still immobile throws the whole timing of the swing out of gear and the body elements are at sixes and sevens with one another.

In view of the above remarks it is essential to find a way of gearing together, all the body elements - legs, hips, shoulders and arms - and so eliminate this prolific cause of mistimed swings. Before discussing this problem, however, I must deal first with certain other matters which are a necessary background to that discussion. First, a few brief remarks concerning the downswing.

The one-piece downswing

To remove all ambiguity, let me make quite clear what I mean by one-piece downswing. It means that the shoulders and arms move in one-piece throughout the downswing. In the first stage the clubshaft participates in this one-piece movement, since it moves as an integral part of the shoulders-arms block in the way already discussed in Chapter III. In the second stage it becomes the second link of the two-link flail described earlier. Thus, the relation between the movement of the shoulders- arms unit and that of the clubshaft follows the same pattern in both the upswing and the downswing, i.e. all one-piece in the first stage with the clubshaft forming a separate link in the second.

The relation between the motion of the shoulders-arms unit and that of the legs-hips unit in the downswing is, however radically different from that in the upswing. For the two units are no longer geared together, the legs-hips unit starting off well ahead of the shoulders-arms, as is very clearly shown Fig. 7. In this are shown some line diagrams, based on photographs of Lloyd Mangrum, a distinguished American professional of a few years ago.

In Fig 7.(a) the player is at the top of the swing – full shoulder turn with left shoulder-point under the chin, hips partly turned to the right, left heel raised and left knee sharply bend inwards and slightly outwards. The initial movement, which changes position Fig 7.(a) into position Fig 7.(b), is a key movement in the downswing and is a characteristic displayed by all good players. Note that although the one-piece movement of shoulders arms and clubshaft has barely started, a major change has already occurred in the position of hips and legs, and this has resulted in a correspondingly major weight shift. For in position Fig 7.(b) the hips have swivelled back to face front again, the left heel has solidly returned to ground and the weight, previously largely on the right foot, is now equally shared by the two feet.

This major change that has come over the substructure (as one may call it) of legs and hips, while the superstructure of shoulders and arms have barely moved, is an essential manoeuvre if the legs and hips are to be in a position to apply power in the downswing. It never occurs if the arms move independently of the shoulders, i.e. if the arms are not content to wait and be carried one-piece with the shoulders. The purpose of the manoeuvre is obvious. It is to establish the hips in the position of being one step ahead of the shoulders-arms unit *throughout the downswing* and so, via the powerful back muscles, to be able to force the shoulders round after them.

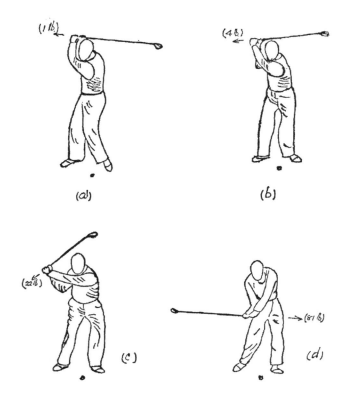

Fig. 7. Outline diagrams from Golf – a New Approach by Lloyd Mangrum

Some writers, in discussing the way the hips lead the shoulders as impact is approached, do the learner a very real disservice by implanting in his mind the mischievous idea that the purpose of this lead is to get the hips out of the way in order to allow the shoulders and arms to apply their hitting power. Nothing could be further from the truth and nothing is more calculated to put the learner on the wrong track, for it suggests that the hit is made by an independent movement of shoulders and arms and that the hips are mere obstructions to be got out of the way for that purpose. Such an interpretation can hardly be further from the true interpretation that the shoulders and arms move only in response to the powerful action of the hips whose lead is essential for that purpose.

To summarise the above remarks, what we have in the downswing is an interaction between three sets of moving units:

(i) the legs-hips unit, which supplies the power for operating the two-link flail of shoulders-arms and clubshaft. The legs-hips unit does not constitute an extra link to form a three-link flail, any more than the biceps muscles controlling the forearm in Fig. 6 (b) constitute an extra link.

(ii) the shoulders-arms unit actuated by the power-generating legs-hips unit,

(iii) the clubshaft.

There is a time-lag between (i) and (ii) and a further time-lag between (ii) and (iii) but there is no time-lag between the elements that constitute any one of these three. For in (i) all the elements are geared together to move in step, in (ii) the elements constitute a single block and the same is naturally true of item (iii).

Whereas the general principle on which the downswing operates is well enough described in the above paragraphs, something more is needed if practical help is to be given to the aspiring beginner. By practical help I mean help to achieve a more efficient swing and thereby a lower handicap. That is the reason for discussing the items that now follow.

Where the power comes from

I want here to demonstrate with your assistance and to your satisfaction that power in the downswing has its source in the legs and hips.

If you compare the position of hands and clubshaft in Fig. 7(d) with their position at F and FJ in Fig 4., you will see that player is applying a force *along the clubshaft* of about 80 lb.

Put yourself in the same position as Fig. 7(d) and see what kind of force you can apply with the clubhead *fixed in some way*. Try first with hips and legs doing nothing except holding themselves fixed in one position, and see what the shoulders-arms unit can do on its own. You will find that, with the hips and legs immobilised, the shoulders and arms are surprisingly feeble and that the idea of applying a force of some 80 lb. is out of the question.

Now fix the right elbow on the right hip and use your legs to slide the right hip towards the target and feel the force at your disposal: you feel you could almost pull the clubhead off its shaft so much force is there. It is clear from this that the slinging action of the hips and legs is the source of power and that the business of the shoulders and arms is to transmit that power to the hands. What is particularly worth noting is the way the right arm sets itself early in the downswing with the right elbow leading as in Fig. 7(c), in order to get that elbow close to the hips when the resistance gets tough in position Fig. 7 (d). This point will be discussed further later on.

The mini-swing as a means of experiencing the feel and the timing of the slinging actions of the hips

As I have emphasised above, correct timing of the swing means that the left heel comes down and weight transfer begins just after the upswing is completed. Then, as the downswing starts, the hips take the lead so that, as they are slung round by the legs, they drag the shoulders and arms around after them.

Now there is a simple exercise, which I call a 'mini-swing' that will enable you not only to understand but to personally experience what correct timing feels like. The mini-swing is just a convenient name for a short swing which, despite its shortness, embodies the essential timing characteristics of a full swing.

The reason why you can get the timing of the mini-swing right so very easily is that use is made of an action with which you are already familiar. As I have mentioned elsewhere in this book, there is no better way of learning an unfamiliar action than to relate it to some familiar action that has the same essential characteristics. The familiar action that I propose to make use of in the mini-swing is that of slinging a weighty

object - say 5 to 10 lb. weight - sideways, i.e. parallel to the line of the feet. The object needs to be fairly heavy, because the throwing action I want to invoke is not instinctive if the object is something light like a cricket ball. A large stone will do admirably.

With arms straight and completely relaxed and hanging freely from the shoulders, hold the stone with your two hands and start swinging the stone to and fro sideways like a pendulum gently to begin with but with increasing amplitude as you prepare to make the final sideways fling to the left. As the shoulders rock to and fro in the preparatory swings, note how your body weight shifts rhythmically from one foot to the other. What I particularly want you to observe closely, however, is what your feet legs and hips do as the hands swing to the right *before the final fling to the left*. Remember that all you have to think about is to sling that stone as far to the left as you can, using the *action that comes natural to you*. At the same time you must observe what that action consists of.

What you will observe is that, as your hands reach the end of their last swing to the right, your left heel returns to ground there and then (assuming that in the preparatory swings the heels have alternately lifted slightly) and the legs and hips take the initiative by sliding to the left and rotating at the same time. This action of the legs and hips provides the power for slinging the stone via the shoulders-arms unit.

Do the exercise over and over again and notice how easy and natural is the sequence of events during the final fling and how unnatural would be any other kind of action.

That does not mean that a different (and wrong) kind of action is not possible. It is possible, and it is highly desirable that you should appreciate, again by direct experience, what that wrong action is, and how it differs from the correct action. Following the preliminary swings to and fro, and just as you are about to make the final fling to the left, time the fling so that your weight comes down solidly on the left heel at the very moment the stone is let loose. It means that shoulders and arms *and* legs and hips move all together in unison, neither group ahead of the other. This is the wrong timing of the legs-hips unit relation to the shoulders-arms unit. You are not tempted to adopt it in the heavy-stone exercise, because the correct timing is also the instinctive timing. That is why I chose this particular exercise; it gives you direct personal experience of the actual feel of wrong and right timing, as different you will find as chalk and cheese.

It is interesting to note that, if a light object - a cricket ball say - had been used, the instinctive action would no longer be to keep the arms straight but to bend them and so introduce a throwing action. That is why the lightness of the clubhead tempts the player to bend his arms in a throwing action, the natural start to which is the abrupt lifting of the club at the start of the backswing. That is also why the bowler at cricket is tempted to use a throwing action by bending his right arm - a temptation that would be non-existent with a heavier ball.

Having absorbed the fundamental idea embodied in the above exercise, you can now try it out with a golf club - still confining yourself to the mini-swing. Choose a heavy club - a sand-iron say - and swing it to and fro preparatory to the final strike. In this case, in order to accentuate the part played by the hip-sling, keep the *elbows pressed close to the body* throughout, the arms straight but the wrists loose to allow cocking and uncocking, and so get the clubhead moving a fair amount with the limited hip movement. Use both the right and the wrong timing as defined above and note that the right method is no longer instinctive, as it was when the heavy stone was used. In fact you may well find that the wrong timing is only too natural and that the right timing is only to be achieved by some degree of concentration.

However, you can always go back to the heavy stone to remind you of the correct timing sequence, should the incorrect sequence begin to bother you. More than anything, you now have the advantage of knowing clearly what you are aiming at and can be your own critic when things go wrong.

There is still of course the main hurdle to overcome, which is to incorporate the correct timing - so easily practised in the mini-swing - into the full-blooded shot. For, the more power you put into the shot the greater is the temptation to use the incorrect timing method, particularly as that is the method you have pretty certainly up till now been using. The matter is further discussed later.

Timing the upswing

When discussing the upswing earlier in this Chapter I referred to the supreme importance of gearing together the movements of all the body elements that take part in the upswing. Thus geared, all parts of the body move in step, each reaching its maximum amplitude at the same moment. By keeping all the movements in step - bending outwards and then inwards of the left knee, rotation of the hips, arching of the small of the back, and turning of the shoulders-arms unit – the timing of the golf swing is profoundly simplified. It is not enough to move the shoulders and arms in one-piece. That one-piece movement must be geared to the legs-hips movement. How, you may well ask, is this gearing to be brought about and what is it like to experience.

There is only one way to deal with that kind of question satisfactorily and that is to resort to the same device as I have used before - make use of a familiar everyday action that embodies most of the essential characteristics of the action in question. The action which satisfies that condition almost one hundred per cent is that of throwing or shying a ball or any small object - an action familiar from childhood and therefore quite instinctive. In a normal throwing action the line of the feet lies at an angle to the line of the target to allow the thrower to make use of both the left and the right side of the back muscles. To make the left side take the lion's share of the muscular effort as it does in the golf swing, the target needs to be square to the line of the feet. Proceed therefore as follows.

Stand upright with feet apart, as in the address position for a drive, and hold some small object in your right hand. Now go through the action of throwing that small object with maximum power towards a distant target squarely in front of you *without shifting your feet*. This simple action, extending from feet to shoulder, closely simulates the muscular co-ordination involved in the upswing in golf. Not only does it simulate the upswing action, it also simulates the kind of action that takes place between the end of the upswing and the start of the downswing. It does not of course duplicate the golf swing action all the way but it does duplicate the nature of that action, from feet to shoulder, in that the same muscles are involved and the same timing. Note in particular:

(i) How perfectly co-ordinated (or geared) are the bending of the left knee, the turning of the hips, the arching of the back and the drawing back of the right shoulder.

(ii) How there is no temptation to sway on to the right foot but rather an inward pressure of the right knee, with the right leg maintaining if not accentuating its original inward slope.

(iii) How you feel energy being packed into the muscles connecting the left hip to the right shoulder as the arching of the back proceeds.

(iv) How you feel that the greater the power you want to put into the throw the further back the right shoulder is drawn and the more pronounced the arching of the back.

(v) How the whole movement is started by a slight reverse movement, i.e. a slight bending of the right knee and a slight turn of the shoulders in the opposite direction. This is analogous to the 'forward press' movement in the swing and is a good way of appreciating the purpose of that method of initiating the main action.

In only one respect does the throwing action above described significantly fail to represent the golf swing and that is the arm action, which introduces an extra link into the flail to make it a three-link-flail action as described earlier in this chapter. So far as the legs, hips, back and shoulders are concerned, however, there is no everyday action that so closely simulates the muscular response to the upswing action in golf and its timing. It gives the learner, *however inexperienced*, the authentic feel of the beautifully co-ordinated movements of those body members in the golf swing. It gives him also a convincing demonstration of the dominant part that a full shoulder turn and an arched back play in generating power.

While the exercise above described throws a useful light on the kind of geared muscular actions that enter into the swing, the right-hand action used in it is very different from the two-handed action of the golf swing. It is therefore necessary to examine in more detail how the hands move in the golf swing, in the confident knowledge that their movement defines also the movement of the shoulders, since shoulders and arms move one-piece. The following paragraphs are therefore concerned with the paths traced out by the hands in both upswing and downswing. They throw a new light on this question and effectively dispose of the confused ideas which have been put forward on this subject in the past.

How the upswing and downswing paths differ both for the hands and for the clubhead and how the hands can be made to follow the right paths

No aspect of the swing is more important than the way the upward and downward paths followed by the hands diverge. For it is a cardinal fact that the paths of the hands and clubhead on the upswing are quite different from their paths in the downswing. This is a natural consequence of the fact that the hips behave quite differently in the two cases - on the upswing they turn gradually and without any sudden change such as there is at the start of the downswing. In the upswing the clubhead follows a path that reaches a much greater height and that sweeps much further behind the head than the path it follows in the downswing. On the downswing the clubhead follows a closer orbit round the body that brings it down along a more direct route than on the upswing. The same remarks apply to the hands, except of course that the up and down paths must in that case reach a common maximum height.

An objective examination of the paths followed by hands and clubhead in the upswing and downswing of top-class players shows up one fact very clearly. This is that the paths followed by the hands hardly vary at all from player to player and that the same conformity applies to the downward path of the clubhead. By contrast, the upswing path of the clubhead varies considerably among top-class players, some taking the clubhead more round the body than others. But in all cases the path of the clubhead on the downswing follows a closer orbit round the shoulders than on the upswing path.

Since it is the paths followed by the hands that are under the direct control of the player, those are the paths I shall here discuss.

It is a fundamental fact, common to all top-class players and to all clubs, woods and irons alike, that there is a clear divergence between the upswing and the downswing paths of the hands. It cannot be better illustrated than by examples taken from action photographs of two well-known professionals - Henry Cotton* swinging a medium iron and Lloyd Mangrum**** swinging a spoon.

---

*   'My swing' (Country Life, 1952)
** See page 39

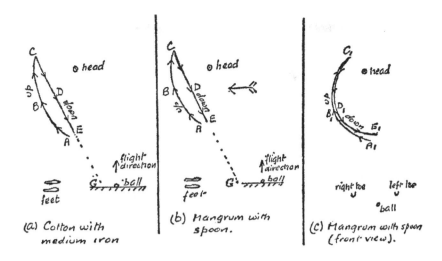

Fig 8. Paths of hands on upswing and downswing

What I have done in each case is to plot the position of the hands in successive exposures and so derive the path followed by the hands in both upswing and downswing, first as seen by a camera facing in the direction of ball travel and second as seen by a camera facing the player. Fig. 8(a) applies to Cotton's swing and Fig. 8(b) to Mangrum's. As you can see, the similarity is remarkable. In each case the hands start their upward path at A and reach the top of the swing C along a climbing path ABC. They descend, however, by a different route CDE, the point E at impact being naturally a little higher and further forward than the starting point A, because the arms are more in line with the shaft at impact - pulled out by the centrifugal force of the clubhead.

To appreciate what is taking place here you need to understand what is meant when a curved path is said to lie in a plane or flat surface. This flat page you are reading is a plane surface and any shape or curve drawn on this sheet is therefore a plane curve. If you look at this plane sheet edge-on (with one eye closed), all you can see is the edge, which appears to you as a straight line. If you draw a curve on the sheet - say a circle - and cut round it with scissors it still looks like a straight line if you hold it edge-on. In fact the test whether or not a curve lies in a plane is to see whether it can be made to appear as a straight line by judiciously turning it round.

The fact that the camera, looking directly along the target line, saw the curve traced by the hands in the downswing as a straight line CDE is proof, first that the curve was traced on a flat surface or plane whose edge is the straight line CDE, and second that this same plane lay *parallel to the target line*. To see the shape of that curve it must be viewed face-on as the camera did when it recorded the front view C1D1E1 of Fig. 8(c).

What is interesting and most instructive is that when the camera viewed the two paths from the front it was hardly able to distinguish the one from the other except for the bottom part of their arcs. Facing the player, the camera could hardly see the ascending path ABC in Fig. 8(a) because, apart from the bit at the bottom, it lay almost dead behind the descending path CDE. That is why in view Fig. 8(c) both the ascending path A1B1C1 and the descending path C1D1E1 were seen by the camera as almost coincident curves - except, as I said above, for the extreme bottom part of their arcs. In general, when the two paths do not coincide, it is the descending path that is on the inside, but they are always pretty close together.

It can be deduced from this that, if the camera had viewed the player not in the direction of the target but along a direction a little to the right of the target (by moving the camera to the left of its position when it took view Fig. 8(a)), it would have seen the ascending path ABC as a straight line and the descending path CDE as a curve bulging to the right.

The whole situation will become crystal clear to you if you can spare a few minutes to construct the simple model I shall now describe.

Cut out a circle of cardboard 5 inches in diameter as shown in Fig 9(d). Draw two chords PR and PS, where R and S are distant 1 inch from the end Q of the diameter PQ. Cut the card along PR and PS and join PR to PS by a strip of cellotape as in Fig. 9(e). Fold along the joint to bring the mid-points of the two arcs to within 1 inch of each other and connect them with a piece of cellotape to keep them that distance apart. The result looks like the half-closed wings of an outsize butterfly. You have now a model which makes the relation between the up and the down paths of the hands in the golf swing perfectly clear when you hold it in the right position. Follow carefully therefore the following instructions.

Place the model straight in front of you and imagine you are looking directly along the line of ball travel (or target line). Now move it about until as in Fig. 9(f) the view you get simulates (except for the bottom part) the view Fig. 8(a) the camera got when facing the target. The folded edge of the model should be so held in position Fig. 9(f) as to make it slope *towards* you as well as slope to the left as shown. What you now see is an edgeways view of the plane in which the descending path CDE lies. It is a plane that lies parallel to the target line, which means that at impact the hands are travelling parallel to that line *as does the clubhead*.

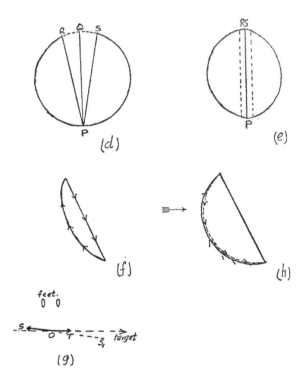

Fig. 9. *Cardboard model demonstrating relation between upswing and downswing paths of the hands*

45

You now see clearly that the ascending path ABC of the hands also lies in a plane - the plane of the rear wing of the model. If you shift your viewpoint a little to the left without moving the model you will get an edgeways view of this plane and you will notice that it points not along the target line but a little to the right of it. This means that the path of the hands as they start from the address position is slightly inside the target line and so also therefore, since the club moves one-piece with the arms, is the path of the clubhead. The advice often given to the learner to start the clubhead 'straight back from the ball', i.e. in line with the target is consequently misplaced - another example in which champion golfers do not practise what they preach. The true situation is illustrated in Fig. 9(g) where the clubhead starts from the ball O along OS, inside the target line, and at impact is moving along OT dead on the target line.

Fig. 9(h) shows how the ascending and descending paths of the hands practically merge together when the model, held in position is looked at in the direction of the arrow i.e. facing the player.

Vital lessons taught by the model

When reading the following paragraphs you should have your cardboard model in front of you and held in position of Fig. 9(f). As a reminder of what that position is, note that

(i)   the folded edge slopes to the left as in diagram and also towards you at a similar angle.

(ii) The front wing, whose plane lies along the target line and whose periphery CDE defines the descending path of the hands, is viewed edgeways and therefore as a straight line.

(iii) The periphery ABC of the rear wing (rear meaning more towards the back of the player) defines the ascending path of the hands and lies in a plane which runs to the right of the target line.

One lesson, and an important one, has already been pointed out i.e. that the path CDE of the hands in the downswing lies in a plane that passes through the target. The fact that the clubhead must be on the target line at impact settles that point. A second lesson is that the ascending path ABC of the hands lies in a plane that does not pass through the target but to the right of it - in the direction of the dotted line OS1 in Fig. 9(g). Since arms, hands and clubhead move as one piece in the takeaway the clubhead also must start on the inside of the target line not much, but definitely inside.

Now it is not so difficult to visualise the descending path when you are actually executing the swing because it is square to your front. Not so the ascending path, however, because it is oblique to your front. The simplest way to visualise it is to think of it as a *plane* arc (i.e. an arc described on a flat surface) just like the descending path but an arc well inside the target line; in other words to think of the arc ABC of the model. Whichever way you visualise the ascending path you have when actually doing the swing, to start the hands (carried of course by the one-piece shoulders-arms unit) on a path that leads inside the line of flight along which they continue until they reach the line of the feet as in Mangrum's upswing in Fig. 8(b). Before they cross the line of the heels they sweep upwards on a more or less vertical path and finally reach the summit C coming forward again.

The practical lesson for you, the average player, to learn here is that you need not hesitate to sweep the hands up on a nearly vertical path once they have crossed the line of the feet. You may feel that you are changing the plane of your swing by doing but in point of fact you will not; because what you will be doing is keeping *in the same plane*, but a plane that is at an angle with the target line and therefore not easily visualised by you. By following this procedure you will be avoiding the dangerous fault to which too many players are prone - of sweeping the hands much too far behind the body. Your model shows you that the plane in which you start the downswing is at an angle to the plane in which you finish the upswing. From moving in a plane that is at an angle to the target line you suddenly switch to a plane that is dead along the target line. Thus the model shows that the two paths form a loop - inside the target line on the way up and on the target line on the way down.

How the paths followed by the hands solves the problem of how to move the shoulders What provides practical justification for the above rather detailed study of the paths followed by the hands in an orthodox golf swing is that those paths govern the whole movement of shoulders and arms. If your hands follow the orthodox paths common to all top-class players in the upswing and the downswing, your shoulders must necessarily rotate about the right axis - so long of course as shoulders and arms move in one-piece, a condition already described as fundamental. As a result you can concentrate on guiding the hands along their proper paths and let the shoulders look after themselves.

There is another point worthy of mention. It concerns the way the plane of descent CDE in Figs 8(a) and 8(b) is related to the ball and to the player. You will note that if that plane is extended, downward as indicated by the dotted line, it meets the ground at G1 on a line parallel to the line of flight but a little closer to the player's feet. With one edge of the plane resting along this line it tilts towards the player at an angle of roughly 65°, cutting him through the middle of the chest.

I have said nothing so far about the path of the clubhead except to point out that, like the hands, its path at the start of the upswing is slightly inside the target line, and at the end of the downswing, i.e. at impact, obviously dead along the target line. A careful plot of the clubhead position in successive film exposures shows that its path in the downswing is practically in the same plane as the path of the hands as one would expect from dynamical considerations. Its path in the upswing is a very different matter and can vary considerably as between one top-class player and another. It depends partly on where in the upswing most of the wrist cocking action takes place and partly on the type of wrist action, both subject to individual preference. For example both Cotton and Nicklaus raise the clubhead high on the backswing - far higher than on the downswing. In Bobby Jones's swing, on the other hand, the head in the backswing goes not much higher than in the downswing. In fact it can be accepted that the path followed by the clubhead in the upswing has little significance and is a matter of personal preference. Thus, the only part of the golf swing that does not follow a common pattern is the upswing path of the clubhead. In all other respects - path of hands on the upswing, path of hands on the downswing and path of clubhead on the downswing - top-class players follow a common pattern very closely.

In the above paragraphs I have gone into the question of the paths followed by the hands and the clubhead in some detail because I consider that every player should have a clear conception of what those paths are. This detailed discussion will also I trust serve a further purpose, which is to correct the views put forward by certain writers, among them Ben Hogan and John Jacobs.

It was Ben Hogan, I think, who first drew attention to the importance of moving the hands and clubhead in the correct planes. Unfortunately, however, his ideas on the subject, as described in his book* are somewhat in error. He is right enough in recognising that the upswing and downswing lie in different planes: where he errs is in getting them the wrong way round. According to him, the upswing path lies in the target plane and the downswing path lies in a plane that passes right of the target - the exact opposite of the facts.

John Jacobs in his book** mentions only one plane - a plane resting on the shoulders in the address position and passing through the ball - and suggests that the learner should strive to keep the clubhead moving in this plane throughout the swing. That this concept cannot be reconciled with the facts hardly needs pointing out in view of what I have said above about the different planes of the up and the downswings. Because of his erroneous ideas on this subject of swing planes he comes to an erroneous conclusion in his analysis of Cotton's swing, which he maintains is 'most characteristic and individual'. He bases this opinion on the fact that Cotton's clubhead goes high up on the backswing. It does indeed, as does that of Nicklaus and many other top-class players, but

---

*   'The modern fundamentals of golf' (Nicholas Kaye, 1957)

** "Golf" (Stanley Paul, 1963)

there is nothing significant about this, since the path of the clubhead on the backswing is the one feature that is individual to *every* player. What Jacobs has failed to recognise is that the paths followed by Cotton's hands in the upswing, by his hands in the downswing and by his clubhead in the downswing are models of orthodoxy. The elevated path of the clubhead in Cotton's upswing has led Jacobs to state that 'just before the clubhead comes to hip height, he lifts hands, arms and club into a different and more upright plane'. The club - yes, but not the hands and arms, which do not change their plane but follow the plane of the ascending path ABC of Fig. 8(a) on the upswing and then come down along the plane CDE of the descending path.

I have treated Jacob's views in some detail because I think it is misleading to give the learner the impression that the modern golf swing is something that can basically vary from one top-class player to another. The evidence of numerous film sequences proves that it does not.

Mental picture of the upswing

I have dealt fairly fully and, I trust, clearly with the paths the hands have to follow in the upswing and the downswing. Although the downswing is the power stroke, it is the upswing that is the crucial factor for success. It is therefore vital that you have a clear mental picture of what you are about when you set it going.

Let me say at the onset that I am convinced that the advice offered by some leading professionals to start in such a way as to make the clubhead move straight back from the ball is responsible for more ruined swings than almost any piece of advice ever offered to the sorely tried learner. You will see what I mean if you do the following exercise. Take up your usual address position with the driver (say) and start the clubhead moving back straight from the ball, and what do you find? You find that you can't make the initial movement of the clubhead straight back from the ball without a *purely rocking* movement of the shoulders, which means dipping the left and raising the right shoulder. It is a movement that conveys no suggestion of an impending powerful winding-up action. Before the clubhead has travelled twelve inches, you have jettisoned all chance of a good swing. It is a real puzzle how such ill-conceived advice ever came to be accepted as helpful. Give me Bobby Jones's advice, which he gives in his latest book*. 'I have always favoured' he says 'a method that brings the club back well away from the line of play - around the body, if you please - because such a stroke has the advantage of *greater power* without sacrificing accuracy ...' How true the italic words!

Since the initial movement in the upswing is so critical, let us examine it in more detail. I have already pointed out the danger of trying to start the clubhead moving straight back from the ball but you need to have a clear understanding of *why* such a start is bad. You have already found in the above exercise that starting in this way causes shoulders to rock but not to turn and lacks any feeling of preparing for a powerful downswing. Note further now its effect on the left knee - how it evokes *no response from the knee* which is free either to remain immobile or to take up a purposeless bend. Note also the response of the hips - just a lateral shift to the right. I have previously emphasised that the body elements concerned in the upswing must all move in gear, so that the movement of one element involves the movements of all. On this count alone, the lack of response from the left knee justifies the view that this method of starting the upswing is essentially unsound.

Now try the right method. Start by unhesitatingly moving the hands (carried by the one-piece shoulder-arms unit) sharply away from the line of flight, until the left arm and the shaft are parallel to the line of flight and vertically above the line of the feet. For the first foot or two of its travel the clubhead is kept low to the ground. Note how this movement *automatically induces bending of the left knee and turning* - not laterally shifting - *the hips.*

---

*   '*Bobby Jones on Golf*' (Cassell, 1968)

It will pay you to practise this method of takeaway - this starting movement of the upswing - until it becomes second nature to you. It will be a priceless asset to you on the first tee in that you do not have to think about how to start; you just implicitly rely on this now familiar movement to carry you safely, at least to the point where the left arm, hands and clubshaft are all parallel to the line of flight and vertically are above the line of the feet.

One little point though. At address, the clubshaft makes an angle with your left arm - what is really a form of initial wrist cock. This angle must not be allowed to straighten out as you start the upswing; in other words, when the hands and left arm reach the line of the feet the shaft is not in one straight line with the left arm but at its original address angle. To preserve the angle requires a slight but quite distinct downward pressure with the heel of the left hand and a corresponding upward pressure with the forefinger of the right hand. Incidentally this is just what Joe Novak advocates in his book*, where he states that this action is a feature common to the swings of all top-class players, as indeed, I can testify from examining a good many records of leading professionals.

A major advantage of starting the upswing with the kind of take-away above described is the fact that the movement of the hands *determines the movement of the arms-shoulders one- piece block*. The mistake that many golf writers make is to tackle the difficult job of defining what the hands do in terms of what the shoulders do. Thereby they commit themselves to describing the movement of the shoulders - how much they tilt and how much they turn as the swing proceeds - a most formidable task. Far simpler is it to describe the movement of the hands thereby short-circuiting the necessity of describing the accompanying shoulder movement.

Having got the initial movement in the upswing - from the address position to the point where the left arm lies parallel to the line of flight - thoroughly taped, it becomes necessary to consider the question of

---

*   'Par Golf' (Herbert Jenkins, 1951)

'Where do you go from there?'

This is where the cardboard model, held in position Fig. 9(f) with its front wing viewed edgeways along the line of flight, can supply the answer. The ascending path of the hands is defined by the peripheral arc of the rear wing plane points right of the target. You see clearly from this and from of Fig. 8(a) and (b) that, following the initial 'round the body' movement, which brings the hands away from the line of flight as far as the line of the feet, the hands *do not cross this line* but sweep vertically upwards until, as they approach the summit of their climb, they move slightly forward again, i.e. back towards the line of flight. Although the path followed by the hands remains in a plane (i.e. flat surface), the fact that that plane lies at an angle with the line of travel of the ball makes it difficult for you to realise that your hands, while moving in the way just described, are actually moving in one plane - on the same flat surface. Unless you can visualise the upward path of your hands as the curved edge of the rear wing of your cardboard model, you tend to get the false impression that you are constantly changing the plane in which your hands are moving, whereas actually you are not.

The following is a summary and reminder of the salient features of the upswing movement:
(i) Start with a shoulder turn, which carries arms, hands and clubshaft in a one-piece movement - left arm straight and clubhead close to the ground.
(ii) The guiding agent in this initial movement is the hands, whose initial path can be visualised as a straight line from their address position to a point above the line of the feet and to the right of the right instep. It will be a curved path of course but it simplifies matters you visualise it as straight.
(iii) Because you are preserving the same angle between the left arm and the clubshaft in the above initial movement, the clubshaft will have reached the horizontal while the left arm is still well short of the horizontal.

(iv) The left knee will automatically bend outward (towards the line of flight) during the above initial movement.

(v) On completing the above initial movement, the hands cease their 'round the body' movement and sweep vertically upwards, carried by a shoulders-arms unit still moving in unison. At the same time the wrists begin their cocking action.

(vi) As the hands approach the top of their swing and the shoulders approach their full turn, the upward sweep of (v) above acquires a slightly forward component to bring the hands back towards the line of flight. This forward component is naturally a little more pronounced In Mangrum's spoon shot of Fig. 8(b) than in Cotton's iron shot of Fig. 8(a) because it is a fuller swing.

(vii) Geared with the above movements of the superstructure of shoulders, arms and hands is the progressive turn of the hips and the progressive bending of the left knee, which after bending forward during the initial stage of the upswing swivels round to bend inward towards the right knee during the final stage.

A final word to minimise the chance of misunderstanding. It concerns the phrase 'shoulder turn', used in (i) above to describe the very first action of the shoulders in starting the upswing. A turn of the shoulders can be made in many ways. Their initial turn *could* be in a horizontal plane, in which case the clubhead certainly *would* start moving straight back from the ball, as you can prove to yourself by simple trial. That is the kind of shoulder turn to avoid, and you will avoid it by the simple expedient of starting the hands in the way already advocated. For, if the shoulders turn in such a way as to make the hands (and clubhead) start by coming away from the line of flight (inside it) while still keeping the clubhead low, they will be turning correctly. Which means that you need only focus your attention on the path followed by the hands to get the shoulder movement right.

The descending path of the hands

I have already made it clear that the downward path of the hands lies in a plane that passes through the target. It is the plane whose edge you see as the straight line CDE in Fig. 8(a), and Fig. 9(f). The change from the plane of the upswing to that of the downswing takes place as the hands leave their summit point C to form the loop I have already spoken of.

In contrast with the upswing path of the hands, the downswing path not only is in one plane but also gives the feeling of *being* in one plane. Its plane is also *shallower* than that of the upswing plane. By shallower I mean that it makes a smaller angle with the horizontal, a fact that is not evident from the side-view diagrams of Fig. 8 but which is crystal clear from the model. Hold the model again in position of Fig. 9 (f) so that you have an edgeways view of the front wing, (whose periphery represents the downward path of the hands and whose plane passes through the target) and an oblique view of the rear wing. Looking at these two planes you cannot say at a glance which is the steeper flat surface. Your difficulty, however, at once disappears if, while holding the front wing fixed you increase the angle between the two wings - you will have to cut the cellotape holding them apart to do so. You then see that, as you increase the angle, the more vertical the rear wing plane (flat surface) becomes. If the folded edge slopes only to the left but not towards you, the rear wing plane becomes dead vertical when the angle between the wings is a right angle. If the folded edge slopes both left and towards you to represent what happens in practice, the rear wing plane becomes dead vertical earlier.

In brief, the greater the angle between the two wings the more vertical the rear wing plane becomes. The upswing path is therefore always on a more vertical plane than the downswing path.

When you look edgeways at the plane of the descending path of the hands, shown as CDE in Fig. 8(a) and (b), you cannot see the shape of the path in that plane, any more than you can see the shape of the periphery of the model wing looked at edgeways. To do that you must view the same plane square-on as in 8(c), which shows the path in relation to the head and feet of the player and to the ball. Viewed this way, you can see that as the hands start down from C1 they also move away from the head to the right. To make the hands do that two conditions need to be satisfied – a full shoulder turn and a straight left arm. If you start the downswing after different amounts of shoulder turn, you will find that, to experience the feeling of the hands moving to the right, requires a full turn with the left shoulder-point well under the chin.

The two components of clubhead speed at impact

One of the interesting results derived via the mathematical analysis of the golf swing, and one of considerable practical importance, is that the speed of the clubhead at impact is made up of two distinct and equal components. What this signifies will be readily understood if you have a look again at Fig 4.

There you see the path ABWFC of the hands as they move from their top position A to their bottom or impact position C. They are carried by a radius arm (representing shoulders and arms) which rotates about the centre O.

At the start the clubshaft AD is fully cocked back relative to the rotating arm OA. That cocking angle is still intact when the hands reach B. Thereafter, however, the angle opens out gradually as the wrists uncock until by the time the impact point C is reached, clubshaft and arm are in one straight line OCL. Thus, it is only after the hands reach B that the clubhead begins its chase of the hands so as to get into line with them by the time impact takes place.

If therefore you visualise an imaginary clubhead that is always in line with the hands, what the real clubhead is doing is chasing that imaginary clubhead so as to catch up with it at impact point. Obviously therefore it has to gain in speed on that imaginary head and this it does to such good effect that when it overtakes the imaginary head at L it is passing it at high speed.

Now what the mathematics shows is that when the real clubhead passes the imaginary in-line clubhead it is travelling at twice the latter's speed. Thus, half the clubhead speed at impact is due to the rate at which it 'whips' past the hands, while the other half is the speed of the imaginary in-line head.

The important lesson to be learnt from this is that any interference with the free hinging action of the hands in the impact region must reduce the 'whip-past' speed and therefore reduce what contributes half of the resultant speed. This shows how futile is the idea sometimes put forward that there should be some slowing down of the left hand to allow the right to 'hit against it'.

To achieve the free hinging action of the hands above mentioned it is necessary for the wrists to remain straight at impact and for some distance beyond during which the right hand gradually climbs over the left while the right arm straightens out. The worst thing that can happen is for the left wrist to bend back after the impact point is passed. I realise that it is all very well to advocate maintaining straight wrists through the impact area. The question is how that is to be achieved.

Before dealing with that question it is necessary to consider the other component half of the clubhead speed at impact - the speed of the in-line imaginary head, which can be regarded as carried by a clubshaft-length extension of the left arm. Being located on an extension of that arm, its speed depends on the speed with which the arm swings round, and this in turn depends upon the rate with which the shoulders are turning. It follows that, if this component half of the total clubhead speed is to be maintained throughout the impact area, there must be *no drop in the rate of shoulder turning* as the bottom arc of the swing is traversed.

We have now established the conditions that must be satisfied if each of the two components of clubhead speed:-

(a) the speed of the imaginary in-line head, and

(b) the whip-past speed,

is to be fully exploited. To exploit speed (a), the shoulders must preserve their rate of rotation throughout the bottom arc of the swing and beyond. To exploit (b) the hands must function as free hinges, so that the shaft can turn round them without restriction. And to achieve this the wrists must be kept straight at and for some distance beyond impact when the right arm straightens out and the right forearm gradually rolls over the left.

What is important for you to appreciate is that the two conditions just mentioned are interdependent. The condition for (b) - keeping the wrists straight - depends on the condition for (a) - keeping the shoulders moving - being satisfied. In fact, it is true to say that, if you keep the shoulders rotating at an undiminished rate over the bottom arc of the swing, there is less temptation to bend the wrists as the right forearm climbs over the left. Once, however, the right shoulder is allowed to slow up as the impact point is approached - the commonest of failings - it becomes very difficult to keep the wrists straight and at the same time roll the forearms to turn the face over in the follow through. What happens in most cases is that the roll of the forearms never takes place, and therefore the clubface never closes but remains at the angle it had at impact. The only alternative way to deal with a slowed-up right shoulder is to perform a 'flick-roll' of the forearms - to close the clubface very quickly after impact with anything but straight wrists, a most reprehensible practice.

It follows from the above discussion that, in order to benefit from both components (a) and (b) of the clubhead speed at impact, the governing requirement is to keep the shoulder rotation - largely a rocking movement going - at an undiminished rate throughout the bottom arc of the swing. Perhaps it is not an exaggeration to say that this is largely what distinguishes good players from average.

The mental picture to visualise is of the right shoulder sweeping down under the chin and driving forward in the follow-through under the motive power of the legs and hips. An alternative way to visualise the action, which is also very effective, is to think of the downswing as a hit with the right shoulder. This focuses attention on keeping the shoulders rotating fast throughout the impact region. There is then every chance that the hip-sling required to power this shoulder movement will automatically come into action.

It is an odd fact, and one worth remarking on, that although the shoulders, arms and hands move in unison in the downswing, the way the downswing is executed depends very much on whether it is the speed of the hands or the speed of the shoulder-turn that the player concentrates on. You might think that it should not matter which you concentrate on, since the one involves the other. But that is not so. If you concentrate on speeding the hands, there is a tendency to quit, once contact with the ball is made. And quitting at contact means that the player is preparing to quit before contact - to the detriment of clubhead speed. Somehow you cannot persuade the hands - really the part of the mind concerned with the hands - to continue moving fast beyond the impact point, as they seem to be convinced the effort would be pointless. Not so the shoulders, which are easily persuaded to go flat out right through the impact point and beyond. That is why, in the downswing, the mind should be focused on developing maximum shoulder rotational speed right through impact and on to the follow-through. The hips are ready to respond to whatever call is made on them. The hands cease their demands at impact but the shoulders insist on the hips carrying on right through.

Importance of right elbow leading the hands in the downswing

Having the right elbow leading the hands in the downswing is something that is universally recognised as conducing to a well-executed golf swing. It is regarded by one American authority as important enough to justify putting on the market a special device of rubber strands supposed to more or less forcibly guide the right elbow along its proper path. One way to keep the right elbow leading is to keep it as close as possible to the left elbow throughout, both in the upswing and in the downswing. This is the basis of a kind of webbing harness which Henry Cotton once advocated as a good training aid by accustoming the player's anatomy to the feel of the right elbow leading in the downswing.

How effective such devices have proved, I have no means of knowing, but it will be accepted, I think, that if the learner can be made to understand the benefit to be derived from having the right elbow leading the hands, he may find the action easier to incorporate in his own swing. The purpose of the following paragraphs is to try and bring about that understanding.

From what has been said previously, you are now familiar with the fact that in the first stage of the downswing shoulders and arms move one-piece - not just geared together but moving together as one solid block. Keeping them moving in a solid block is not, however, any sort of guarantee that a proper start will be made in the downswing. For, despite doing so, it is still possible, indeed fatally easy, to start the downswing with too much turning and too little rocking of the shoulders, i.e. the left shoulder moving back (away from the line of flight) instead of moving upward and along the target line.

Now, the action of the right elbow leading the hands as soon as the downswing starts is a powerful deterrent against the wrong shoulder movement just mentioned. There is no need for you to accept this statement without proof, and the proof is best provided by a simple exercise which you can do yourself. Take up the top-of-the-swing position shown in Fig.7(a) as nearly as you can, with the clubshaft horizontal and in line with the target. Don't mind if your right elbow is sticking out somewhat - just let it take up a comfortable position. I want you to do the wrong shoulder movement first, so that you can appreciate the contrast when you do the right movement. With the right elbow still sticking out, make therefore a small turn of the shoulders - no rocking but a purely horizontal turn and watch what happens to the left shoulder, to the hands and to the clubhead. You will note that the left shoulder-point moves back, your hands move forward (towards the line of flight) and the clubhead moves directly backward - a most effective start for an outside-to-in downswing and therefore a sliced shot. Now for the correct start, in which the first movement of the right elbow is towards the left elbow and inwards to the right side, so bringing the right forearm into a vertical position. In other words the correct start is to bring the elbows closer together. Note how the left shoulder automatically responds to this kind of elbow movement by moving upwards and not backwards as before. At the same time the hands move downward and to the right in the authentic descent path described earlier, while the clubhead (visible in a mirror) moves upward as well as backwards. In both the wrong and the right start to the downswing, only the small initial movement needs to be made in the above exercise.

Two other desirable results follow as a natural consequence of the right elbow leading the hands. One is the initial hip shift which changes position Fig 7. (a) into position Fig 7. (b). The other is the superior position one is in later in the downswing for applying the heavy pull required to overcome the rapidly growing resistance met with at that stage.

Study again the classical style of Lloyd Mangrum in Fig 7 (a), (b), (c), and (d). Note particularly how the right elbow is already well in the lead halfway down in position (c) and how favourable it is placed in position (d) for coping with the 80 lb. resisting pull of the clubhead at that stage. Obviously, the transmission of force from shoulders to hands in position Fig. 7(d) is heavily dependent on the right arm, and a right arm with a sticking-out elbow is hardly ideally placed for the job.

Recommended further reading

What I have tried to do in this chapter is to give the learner a better understanding of the golf swing, basing my points partly on the conclusions reached via the mathematical analysis described in the earlier chapters, partly on action photographs of top-class players and partly on what I like to think is a modicum of logical thought. The idea of describing certain aspects of the swing in terms of familiar everyday actions has been freely used, for I am of the opinion that far too little use has been made of this effective kind of approach in the past.

Anyone who wants to study other aspects of the golf swing beyond the somewhat limited and specialist coverage given to it here should, in my view, ponder over what Bobby Jones has to say in his two books 'Golf is my game' and 'Bobby Jones on golf,' to both of which I have already had occasion to refer.

CHAPTER VI

DOES THE SWING ITSELF - AS DISTINCT FROM ITS SPEED - DEPEND ON PHYSICAL STRENGTH?

L et me make clear what is meant by the phrase 'the swing itself' as used in the above chapter heading. By 'the swing itself' I mean *the successive positions through which the club and the hands and arms pass through in the course of the downswing.* In the case of Bobby Jones's swing the positions passed through are shown in the photograph of Fig. 1 or, in diagrammatic form, in Fig 2. These define the swing itself. Note that *unless the camera speed is specified* these figures tell us nothing about the speed at which the whole swing was performed. In other words, the speed at which this sequence of positions were passed through is something quite distinct from the sequence itself.

To make sure that you understand what I am driving at, a simple example will suffice. You have seen a man knocked down in a televised boxing match but, because of the speed of the punch, you were not sure exactly how it happened. However, immediately afterwards in a slow-motion repeat you were able to see the precise way in which the punch was delivered. Now the motion was exactly the same in both cases and only the speed of its performance was different. In other words, the course followed by the boxer's fist (and arm) in landing the blow were unaltered, only the speed was different. The same thing applies to the golf swing; the swing itself is one thing, its speed itself is quite another. The swing itself, being merely a sequence of positions passed through, is something independent of muscular force. A small boy, wielding a club to suit his size and strength can be taught the authentic golf swing used by Hogan, Snead, Cotton and all the other giants of the game. His swing will be slower indeed but the swing itself will be essentially the same. What the small boy lacks is physical strength, but this only affects the speed of his swing and thereby the distance he gets: his lack of strength does not prevent him from using the one and only orthodox swing of the masters.

In case someone thinks that there is something about a powerful golf swing that makes it difficult or impossible to reproduce at a slower tempo I need only call attention to a certain elementary principle of dynamics. This states that the force necessary to swing or throw any free object – a club, racket, javelin, cricket ball or what have you - is directly proportional to the square of the speed given to it. If the speed is increased in the ratio 3 to 2 the effort must go up in the ration 3 (squared) to 2 (squared) or 9 to 4. Correspondingly, at 2/3 of the true speed the muscular effort is down to 4/9. The effort, in other words, changes much faster than the speed, so that by slowing an action down a little the force required drops much faster. Correspondingly, of course, any gain in speed is dearly bought by a more than proportionate increase in effort.

It follows from this that if a woman player has (say) 64% of a man's strength she can swing the *same* club at 80% of the man's speed and get 80% of his length. She does this by going through exactly the same motion - performing the self-same swing - as the man but using at all stages only 0.64 or about 2/3 of his effort. This leads us to the fundamental conclusion that a woman player can, in all essentials, faithfully copy the authentic swing of the masters by simply executing it at a slower tempo.

The sequence of positions in the swing used by the masters is the sequence, more than all others, that enables them to exploit their physical power to the best advantage. To use the same efficient swing a woman has only to reduce its tempo to suit her physical strength.

It might be thought that what I have been at some pains to demonstrate in the above paragraphs is fairly self-evident. For, after all, a technique of swinging is a technique and therefore teachable to anybody whatever his or her physical strength, The reader however has only to delve a little into existing golf literature to find that what he might think should be self-evident is far from self-evident to certain writers on golf.

As this is a matter of some importance I propose to show why those writers - among them John Jacobs - have fallen into error. A prime reason is the undoubted fact that many, if not most of the best women players use a swing that differs in one important aspect from the standard swing used by all top-class men players. The difference is that women players start to uncock their wrists earlier in the downswing than men. There is clear-cut evidence of this in a film sequence contained in a book by the late Pam Barton, who was undoubtedly a top-class player. At a point in the swing where the left arm has reached the horizontal position, and where a top-class man player would have his wrists still fully cocked, the film shows Pam Barton's wrists to have already started to uncock. This is clearly shown in Fig. 10(a) and (b) which are outline copies[*] of two pictures from the film in question. These should be compared with the two outlines Fig. 10 (c) and (d) of Bobby Jones at the same stage in the downswing.

The positions of the hands and arms relative to the body are practically identical for the two players, but it is clear that the wrist process has gone further in pictures (a) and (b) than in (c) and (d).

In contrast, compare Fig. 10(d) of Bobby Jones with Fig. 7(d) of Lloyd Mangrum at the same stage in the downswing. The positions of the hands and clubshaft relative to the body are practically indistinguishable, as they would be if compared with any other top-class player. There is one of Cotton's for example - picture No. 14 of his film sequence[**] for the driver. This is an almost exact replica of Lloyd Mangrum in Fig. 7(d). Such comparisons could be multiplied 'ad lib' and they go to show that while all first-class men players use the same swing most women players, even in the top-class, use a different swing.

---

[*] *Reproduced by kind permission of Messrs Blackie and Company from the book 'A stoke a hole' by Pam Barton (1937)*

[**] *'My Swing' by Henry Cotton (Country Life, 1925).*

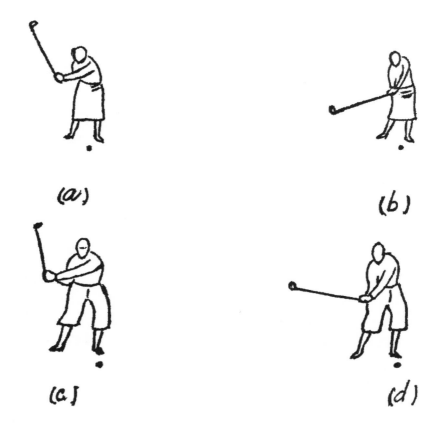

Fig 10. Uncocking of wrists by Pam Barton – (a) and (b), and by Bobby Jones – (c) and (d)

John Jacob's reference to this fault in women's swing occurs in his book 'Golf' (Stanley Paul, 1963). He remarks as follows 'Even the best of them (the ladies) usually begin to uncock the wrists earlier in the downswing than men *need* in order to reach maximum speed at impact. This is simply because their wrists are not so strong as men's are'.

Note the word *need* (my italics) and the dogmatic statement that earlier uncocking in women's swing is due to lack of strength in the wrists. In view of what I have already said above regarding the role of physical strength in relation to the swing itself (i.e. the sequence of positions of hands and club), Jacob's explanation is quite untenable.

Whatever the reason for early uncocking of the wrists by women players may be, one thing is certain. It is not because of lack of physical strength, since physical strength governs only the tempo of the swing and hence the power developed and the distance reached.

To hazard an opinion of the cause, I would say that over-swinging is the most likely cause. In no action photograph of distinguished men players - not even of Nicklaus - have I ever seen a case where the hands at the top of the swing have got even as far round as to be in line with the head when viewed from the front. Yet Pam Barton's hands at the top of the swing are some nine inches beyond that point; she practically turns her back to the ball, whereas men go no further than to turn their backs to the hole. The result is that the first stage of the downswing is much extended and invites departure from the one-piece movement it should be. To deal successfully will such a prolonged first stage the pull of the hands in the initial movement would need to be measured in ounces, for even in Bobby Jones swing it is only a couple of pounds. But to limit the pull at the start of the downswing to a few ounces is hardly on the cards when a strong young woman is intent on sending the ball a long way. Exceeding those few ounces generates excess of centrifugal force in the clubhead and her wrists are quite unable to cope with its strong and premature uncocking action.

You might argue that this merely raises the further question 'Why do women overswing'? Again, hazarding an opinion, I would suggest the reason to be the use of clubs that are too heavy. It is a fact that women's clubs weighing less than 12 oz. cannot be bought from stock - a strange fact when powerful players like Nicklaus use only 13.5 oz. clubs. The answer would seem to be lighter and better designed clubs, a subject discussed later in this book.

Adverting to the subject of overswinging by women, I recall a rather illuminating phrase which Ted Dexter once used when giving his impression in the 'Observer' of a ladies' championship competition. It seemed, he said, as if the club was swinging the player and not the player the club!

CHAPTER VII

WHAT HAPPENS AT IMPACT

It may be thought that what happens at impact is of little interest to a player, since his effort to generate clubhead speed must be completed by the time contact with the ball is made. This is not true, however, because awareness of what does happen at impact can affect his mental attitude to the swing as a whole, as I hope to demonstrate.

It is now common knowledge that the time during which the ball is in contact with the face is about 4/10,000 of a second, and since the clubhead is travelling at 166 ft/sec. before impact and 114 ft/sec. after, thus giving an average speed while in contact of 140 ft/sec., the distance it travels during contact is only 2/3 of an inch. These are well authenticated figures obtained by Messrs Spalding & Company relating to Bobby Jones's swing. It is easy to calculate from them and from the speed of 225 ft/sec. gained by the ball that the peak force between ball and face reaches about 1.5 tons.

The magnitude of the force is admittedly of only incidental interest to a player but the fact that it operates for only 4/10,000 of a second is of considerable importance. This has to do with the velocity with which sound travels along a steel bar or tube. This velocity is about 16,000 ft/ sec. (3 miles per second), so that if a bar 16,000 feet long is given a tap at the near end, the far end would know nothing about it for a whole second. Furthermore, the near end cannot possibly know whether the far end is fixed or free until the sound wave has been reflected back. It takes therefore two seconds for the near end to know what kind of reaction there was at the far end. This is as much as to say that until two seconds have passed the near end cannot possibly be influenced by what happened at the far end in response to the initial impulse at the near end.

In the case of a golf club an impulse lasting only 0.0004 sec. is applied to the clubhead by impact with the ball. A wave runs up the shaft at 16,000 ft/sec. and after reflection runs back towards the head. The time taken to complete the double journey of about 7 ft. is 7/16,000 or 0.00044 sec. so that the clubhead is on the point of losing contact with the ball before it can possible be influenced by what happened at the other end of the shaft

It is clear from this that whichever way the club is held - in a vice-like grip or not - is all one to the ball, for it will have gone before the message from the hands can reach it.

The simple scientific fact that what the clubhead does to the ball is independent of the degree of firmness with which the club is held at the moment of impact can have a profound effect on the mental attitude of the player to the swing. If he believes, as some writers maintain, that it is essential to have a firm grip at impact in order to meet the shock and to maintain pressure on the ball while in contact with the clubface, the inevitable bracing of the muscles that follows is bound to upset the rhythm of the whole swing. Writers who give such advice do a great disservice to the learner who is already over-conscious of the inertia of the ball.

What needs to be impressed on the learner is the scientific fact that, from the very first touch between ball and clubface, he can do nothing further to influence the result. He must therefore ignore the ball or tell himself that it is just a piece of paper made to look like a ball and then concentrate on seeing how fast he can swing the clubhead *through* that piece of paper. In other words the swing to use is the daisy-cutting swing - not the casual swing which that notion conjures up but a determined effort to swing *through* it as fast as possible.

This is not a new idea, for the beginner has often been urged not to be afraid of the inertia of the ball but treat it like a daisy. The fact that such advice is fully endorsed by scientific fact may help the beginner to take it seriously.

The Great Danger of 'Pressing'

This is a good place to issue a much-needed warning on the subject of 'pressing'. In golfing parlance a player is said to press when he tried to inject too much force into a stroke or more force than he can control. It is generally assumed that the temptation to press occurs only occasionally, such as at a longish short hole where the green is guarded by a front bunker. This assumption is wrong, for the truth of the matter is that the average player presses almost on every shot he makes - certainly off the tee on most four and five - shot holes.

The effect on his game of this constant pressing is nothing less than disastrous and it would be fair to say that no surer way exists of knocking several strokes from his handicap than to resist this ever-present temptation

Let me particularise. I said above that the ideal attitude to adopt when preparing for a shot is to regard the ball as a piece of paper through which the clubhead is to pass at maximum speed. 'Ah,' you will say, 'will not the idea of maximum head speed invite the very trouble one is trying to avoid.' Curiously enough, not so. There seems to be a psychological distinction in one's mind between trying to achieve maximum clubhead speed and trying to achieve maximum distance.

I will tell you why I know this to be a fact. As a matter of personal experience I have proved conclusively that it is far easier to reproduce the accepted characteristics of a respectable swing - good follow-through, etc. - when hitting full-blooded shots into a practice net than when hitting the same full-blooded *practice* shots out on the course. I have emphasised the word 'practice' in case you might think that nervous tension has anything to do with it. The fact is that, when hitting into a net the question of distance does not enter one's mind and it is then easy to concentrate on clubhead speed alone. Once out on the course, however, even only practising by oneself, it is somehow impossible to ignore the fact that distance is your true objective. The conscious mind knows well enough that it is only necessary to generate maximum clubhead speed to achieve maximum distance. The subconscious unfortunately is not convinced and has its own ideas about swinging for distance. It usually prevails.

The only solution is for the player to have enough strength of mind to imagine he is still at the practice net when he makes his shots on the course. It is hard but it can be done.

Shaft distortion caused by the impact

A clubshaft is a structural element which takes the form of a tapered tube, and to investigate the behaviour of such an element under applied forces is a job for the structural analyst. He alone therefore is in a position to explain how a clubshaft behaves following impact between clubhead and ball. Yet one finds that plenty of professional golfers, whose knowledge of such matters is less than profound, are ready to air their views on the subject. An example of this is the wrong interpretation of action photographs that show shaft distortion caused by impact. The result is to build up a false picture of what really happens and therefore to mislead their readers. The way the clubshaft does behave under impact with the ball will I trust be made clear from the following paragraphs.

Let us therefore have another look at the photograph of Fig. 1. Attention has previously been called to the fact that bending of the clubshaft is most pronounced at the 10th exposure counting back from the ball and that it straightens out in another 4 exposures, i.e. in 4/100 or 1/25 second. Now, when a pendulum bob is displaced sideways and let go it returns first to the straight-down position, then swings to the other side, then back to the mid-position and finally to the side it started from, thus making a complete oscillation. It follows that the time to return to the mid-position from the initially displaced position is 1/4 of the time for a complete oscillation. The same applies to the bent shaft, the time to return to the straight, i.e. 1 /25 second is 1/4 of the time for a complete oscillation, which is therefore 4/25 or very nearly 1/6 sec.

Now one oscillation in 1/6 sec. is the same as 6 oscillations per second. Now place a driver on a table so that all but some 6 inches of the grip overhangs the edge and clamp down hard on the grip with the left hand while giving the clubhead a sharp tap with the right. The head will oscillate as in Fig. 11 (a), which speaks for itself and you can count the number of oscillations per second roughly. You will find the number to be about 6 per second, which agree exactly with the behaviour of the shaft in the photograph. This is how the club will always vibrate if clamped at the grip.

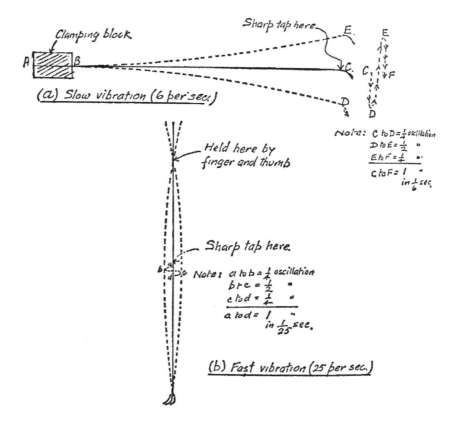

Fig 11. Slow and fast vibration shapes of driver

The shaft vibration caused by sudden impact with the ball is an entirely different type of vibration than that just described. Vibration caused by sudden impact can be observed at leisure if the shaft is held between forefinger and thumb at a point some 8 or 9 inches from the butt end with the head hanging straight down as in Fig. 11(b). In that position, if the shaft is struck a sharp blow at its middle, you will be able to observe this different type of vibration. It is faster than the previous one and too fast for you to count - about 25 oscillations per second. It is this type of vibration that is set up by impact with the ball and it ignores the presence of the hands.

This faster vibration can be clearly observed in the photograph of Fig. 1 immediately after impact. In the first exposure after impact the shaft is bent back, it is straight again and in the next one after that it is bent fully forward. This is exactly half a complete oscillation and it takes only 2/100 sec. A complete oscillation therefore would take 4/100 or 1 /25 sec. to give 25 oscillations per second. This agrees very satisfactorily with the simple experiment described above with the grip held between finger and thumb and the shaft hanging freely.

The reader will be interested at this point to see how wrong ideas gain currency. For suppose that, instead of exposures at 1/100 intervals as in Fig. 1, an ordinary cine-camera was used with 1/25 sec. intervals between exposures. If the slower camera showed the shaft in the second position *before* impact in Fig. 1 it would miss out the following three and would next show the shaft in the 3rd position *after* impact. The existence of the sudden backward bend immediately after impact and the straightening out in the next exposure - the real clues to what is happening - would never be credited and only the forward bend in the 3rd exposure after impact would be seen. This could easily give *the impression that the shaft was in process of flexing forward at impact.*

That is just the mistake made by Henry Cotton whence remarks[*] in respect of an action photograph of himself showing the shaft bent

---

[*]   'My golfing album', *Country Life*, 1959.

forward after impact 'This shaft really helped me in this shot'.

Such misinterpretation unfortunately has side effects, in that it confirms his readers in the all too prevalent view that flexing of the shaft can add power to a shot. The result is that they waste time and money in the quest for a club with the kind of flexibility that will help them in the way that Cotton said he was helped.

It will thus be seen that the points made in this chapter are not merely of academic interest. They are practical points whose importance can be measured in terms of time and money.

CHAPTER VIII

AN INSTRUCTIVE EXERCISE IN TIMING AND SOME IMPORTANT CONCLUSIONS

It is a matter of common observation that certain familiar everyday actions, although requiring meticulous timing, are yet performed with unconscious ease. This suggestion that a good way to achieve correct timing of an unfamiliar action might be to make use of a similar, but less unfamiliar, action whose timing presents little difficulty. The more closely associated the two actions are, the greater the facility with which the lesson learnt in performing the more familiar action can be applied to the performance of the less familiar. As an example, a child that has played about with a scooter has little difficulty in riding a bicycle, and there is little doubt that the quickest and most painless way for an adult to learn to cycle is to spend half an hour experimenting with a child's scooter.

The action that I propose as embodying in all essentials the principle of the golf swing is the simple action of slinging a weight attached to a piece of string to the maximum distance. In doing this, the weight is swung round the head with the right hand in the same plane as that used for the golf swing. A weight of about 6 oz. tied to about a yard of string will do admirably for the purpose.

To justify the parallel drawn between slinging this weight and swinging a golf club it is only necessary to consider again the action represented by Fig. 2. Here the whole purpose of the first stage of the downswing, during which the hands travel from A to B, is to enable them to arrive at point B with such a velocity as can be maintained constant over the arc BC without applying any leverage with the hands and *with the shaft therefore subjected to no force other than a straight pull along it.* The hand velocity reached at the end of the first stage (point B) must be just right to suit the strength of the particular player, i.e. it must be fast enough to require his full strength to keep that velocity up over the remaining arc BC of the swing but neither faster nor slower than this for optimum results.

In the case of the sling (i.e. weight on string) the condition that the force applied must be directed along the string is *automatically satisfied.* The other condition, that the velocity of the hands at B must be such as to allow the operator to use his full strength over the arc BC can only be satisfied by his sense of timing.

Since the sling cannot be raised into the starting position like a club it must be brought into that position by swinging it over the head and shoulders. After a little experimentation the tempo of the backward swing round the head can be gauged well enough to develop a hand velocity at B that is just right for enabling the player to apply maximum hand pull later in the swing.

What is important is the fact that the action of swinging a club and that of swinging the equivalent sling (meaning by 'equivalent' the appropriate weight and string length) are identical actions so far as the second stage of the downswing is concerned. The only real difference is that, whereas the clubhead reaches point B from a stationary initial position at A, the sling weight reaches it from a moving position.

Having made up a sling one can carry out some instructive experiments. Much can be learnt without actually hurling the weight away. Try first a few dummy swings, initiated by circling the right hand clockwise and allowing the weight to pass round the back of the head. The faster this circling action the greater is the velocity gathered by the weight as it enters the second stage of the downswing. It will be found after a few trials that there is an optimum speed for starting the downswing. By which I mean that there is a certain speed for entering the downswing that enables you to apply full power later in the swing.

Entering at too high a speed makes it impossible for the hand to keep ahead of the weight later in the downswing - the weight overtakes the hand to give the same effect as premature uncocking of the wrists when swinging a club

Entering the downswing at too slow a speed on the other hand means that the correct speed is only reached when there is too short an arc of travel left for applying full power. Such effects become obvious after experimenting with various speeds.

The instructive features of such experimentation may be listed as follows:-.

(i) It brings home the fact that the heavy pull - the pull that gives clubhead speed occurs late in the downswing.

(ii) It demonstrates conclusively that it is possible to convert muscular power into clubhead velocity by applying no force other than a force directed along the straight line joining the hands to the clubhead.

(iii) One is extremely sensitive to the 'feel' of the whirling weight throughout the downswing - more sensitive than to the feel of the clubhead when swinging a club. Yet no leverage is, or possibly can be, exerted by the hands, which obviously apply only a simple pull along the string. This *exposes the fallacy of believing thar some degree of flexibility in a clubshaft is needed for 'feeling' the clubhead*. For here we have what is equivalent to a dead straight stiff shaft and yet no closer sympathy between hand and weight can be imagined.

The similarity between swinging a golf club and swinging a weight on a string was long ago pointed out by Ernest Jones with his 'penknife and handkerchief' demonstration. Cotton refers to this in his book* and indicates that he is not entirely convinced, because he ends with the remark 'What I have not grasped is his interpretation of how to swing the clubhead'. The one-piece

---

*   'This Game of Golf', Henry Cotton (Country Life, 1948).

first stage of the orthodox golf swing has admittedly no parallel in the whirling weight, but the second stage - the stage where two-thirds of the clubhead velocity is generated and nine-tenths of the work is done - is identical both in speed and power.

It follows from what has been said above that, so far as the generation of clubhead speed is concerned, the fundamentals of the golf swing are faithfully embodied in the whirling-weight action. I do not wish to sound dogmatic but this settles for good and all the age-old controversy as to whether the golf swing is a true swing or a hit. Its dynamical identity with the whirling weight stamps it as a true swing. The reason why certain players are said to punch their iron shots is that the one-piece first stage of the swing is curtailed by such players, making is necessary for them to gather the necessary hand speed for entering on the second and swinging stage of the swing over a very much shortened arc. Indeed, the very fact that it is centrifugal force and not hand leverage that whips the clubhead into line with the hands at impact stamps the action as a true swing.

Fast hand action and fast swings

Perhaps this is a suitable place for deploring the use of such meaningless phrases as 'fast hand action'. For let it be clearly understood that, if this phrase means high speed travel of the hands in the second stage (the so-called hitting area), then it merely means a fast downswing - synonymous with high clubhead speed and long hitting. So what is the point of coining an unnecessary phrase to confuse the learner? There are far too many ill-defined terms in the literature of golf and, as the political phrase goes, 'they are increasing and ought to be diminished'. What, for example, do you understand by 'slow swinger' and 'fast swinger'? If these terms applied to the downswing they would be identical with short hitter and long hitter and the tyro might well be pardoned for not realising that in most cases slow and fast in this connection apply only to the upswing. I said 'in most cases', because slow and fast are terms sometimes used to denote a leisurely and less leisurely start of the downswing, in other words a longer and shorter one-piece first stage. And so it goes on, to the confusion of the learner's mind.

Finally, have a go at the simple weight-on-string experiment: a lot can be learnt from it.

CHAPTER IX

HOW CLUBHEAD WEIGHT AFFECTS THE SWING AND THE DISTANCE THE BALL TRAVELS

A subject that is a constant source of controversy in the correspondence columns of golf periodicals is the effect of clubhead weight on the distance the ball can be hit. This is somewhat surprising, because it is possible to settle most of the points at issue by an appeal to elementary mechanics. It is possible for example to settle which of two courses is most likely to pay dividends in the matter of achieving greater distance - to reduce the average clubhead weight or to increase it. If the change in weight is no more than an ounce or two it can be said categorically that the advantage is heavily in favour of reducing head weight.

Let us suppose that a player has got used to a 7 oz.-clubhead driver. If he adds an ounce to this he is certainly not going to be able to swing an 8 oz. head faster than he did the 7 oz. nor even swing it at the same speed. The question then remains whether the heavier head can make up for the reduced speed with which it can be swung. What he can do of course is to find out by actual trial whether he can get any extra distance this way. But a simple calculation can save him the bother of such a trial and the inevitable disappointment. For, if it is assumed that he uses the same muscular effort to swing the heavier club the laws of mechanics prove that he will lose rather than gain distance.

For example, if our hypothetical player can drive 200 yds. with the 7 oz head and is able to swing the 8 oz. head *just as fast* he will gain only

5 yds. When, however, account is taken of the inevitable slowing down of the swing the resultant effect is a drive of 194 yds. - net loss of 6 yds. Still heavier heads lead to still greater loss of distance as will be shown later in this chapter.

Since there seems no future for the use of heavier clubheads it is worth considering whether anything is to be gained by using lighter heads. The case *for* using lighter heads however is a lot more complicated than the case *against* using heavier heads, because certain factors have to be taken into account when considering a reduction of head weight which do not enter when an increase in weight is considered. This is particularly true if the change is more than an ounce or two. Let me explain.

Suppose our 7 oz.-head, 200-yard-distance man elects to try the effect of a 6 oz. head. He can obviously swing a little faster with the lighter head and calculation shows that with the *same muscular force applied to the club* he can swing 8% faster, so boosting his drive by 9 yards. Note that I have emphasised the phrase 'applied to the club'. This qualification is necessary because moving the club 8% faster means that the tempo of the swing has also to be that much faster. In other words, every part of the player's anatomy - hips, shoulders and arms - have all to move 8% faster. As, however, swinging the lighter head 8% faster requires no more force, there is no real reason why he should not move his body the necessary 8% faster and so reap the benefits of an extra 9 yards on his drive, particularly when it is remembered that the 260 yard man regularly swings 30% faster even without benefit of a lighter head.

All very well, you may say, but what about going a step further and take 2 oz. off the 7 head? Calculation now shows that, using the *same force as before*, he needs to swing 18% faster and the yardage bonus is 18 yards. If he cannot swing that much faster despite the light 5 oz. head his bonus drops correspondingly. An overweight player might well be able to swing the lighter no more than 9% faster, in which case he would be back where he started - 200 yards, the same as he previously obtained with the 7 oz. head. On the other hand, an athletic type of player might have no difficulty in achieving the faster body motion demanded by a 5 oz. head and therefore be able to earn the 18 yards bonus.

Considerations like these lead one to the conclusion that lighter head than the average in present use will pay handsome dividends to the lightly built athletic type of player and to most women players. Most normally-built players also stand to gain by the lighter clubhead, but the benefit to be obtained by the more heavily built and slower-moving player is less certain and for him a trial-and-error procedure alone meets the case.

That the 18% faster swing, which is the price of an 18 yards bonus, demands no special degree of quickness of movement is clearly proved by the fact already mentioned that all long hitters swing about 30% faster without the benefit of a lighter head.

The reader must not think however that, in order to reap the benefit of a lighter head, all he has got to do is to walk into the pro's shop and ask him to take a couple of ounces off the head of his driver. For one thing, there is hardly that much lead in the average head - an ounce perhaps, but certainly not two ounces, unless the brass base-plate is also dispensed with for the purpose of the experiment. Let us suppose that this is done and the original 7 oz. head now weighs only 5 oz. You sally out to the practice ground to see, once and for all, whether the promised 18 yards extra distance is going to materialise or not. I can tell you what will happen. The first shot with the 5 oz. head will convince you that extra distance or no extra distance, you could not possibly play with such a club. Instead of the usual solid contact with the ball, you feel as if you had hit the ball with a headless driver - the shaft vibrating in your hand in a most disconcerting manner. You decide there and then that light clubheads are not for you and are only too glad to go back to your well-tried 7 ouncer.

This no doubt is the reason why clubs with lighter heads have never come into vogue and why today there are no clubs on the market - not even women's clubs - lighter than 12 oz., which usually means a 6 oz. head on a 6 oz. shaft. This however does show that a 6 oz. head is a practical proposition if matched with a correspondingly lighter shaft. Golf manufacturers have presumably not thought it worthwhile to strive after a still lighter head since to achieve it needs shafts of special design. In my opinion such special design of shafts would be worth the extra trouble and would be a godsend to women players. What is required is a little applied science and not an expensive (and mostly futile) trial and error approach.

It may be of interest to readers to see how dearly long hitters have to pay for the extra distance they achieve.

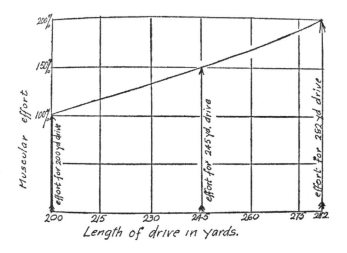

Fig. 12. How muscular effort increases with increasing length of drive, with effort for 200 yard drive reckoned as 100 per cent

Fig. 12 shows how muscular effort increases as length of drive increases from 200 yards to 282 yards. The effort for a 200 yard drive is taken as a basis of comparison and reckoned as 100%. As the yardage increases the curve gradually steepens so that length becomes increasingly costly in muscular effort. A 245 yard drive requires half as much effort again as that for a 200 yard drive and the effort for a 282 yard drive is 200% or double that for the 200 yard drive. Even that is not the whole story, for the 282 yard drive not only requires twice the muscular effort required by a 200 yard drive, it demands in addition a 40% faster swing. In other words the 282 yarder requires twice the effort of the 200 yarder to be packed into about 3 /4 of the time, so that the rate of doing work (horse-power) is nearly three times greater.

It is lucky for the weaker brethren that distance is not proportionate to muscular effort, for if that were the case the long hitter who now achieves a 282 yard drive would reach 400 yards.

The lesson to be learnt from the above remarks is that there is no substitute for brute force efficiently applied.

In order to settle arguments which are for ever appearing in the golfing press about the relative merits of increasing or reducing clubhead weight, Figs. 13 and 14 are here presented. They are simple graphs easy to understand.

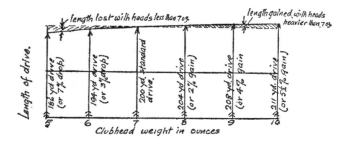

Fig 13. Length of drive with different clubhead weights
swung at same speed; 7 oz. taken as yardstick

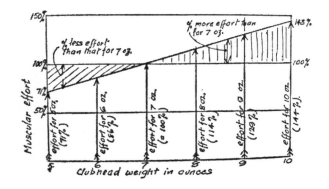

Fig 14. Muscular effort to swing clubheads of different weights
at same speed, counting effort for 7 oz. as 100 per cent

Fig. 13 shows what happens to the length of drive when clubheads of different weights are swung with the *same speed*, assuming, for the sake of argument, that 200 yards is obtained with a 7 oz. head. When an ounce is taken off the 7 oz. head it is seen that the loss of distance with the 6 oz. head is only 6 yards and the loss for a 5 oz. head is no more than 16 yards. Remember however that this assumes the 5 oz. head to be swung no faster than the 7 oz. so that there is a large reserve of power.

How futile it is to opt for heads heavier than 7 oz. is amply demonstrated by the part of the curve beyond the 7 oz. mark. You note that even if a 10 oz. head is swung at the same speed as the 7 oz., the gain in distance is only 11 yards. It is obvious, however, that adding 3 oz. to a 7 oz. head is bound to seriously reduce clubhead speed, so that a net loss in distance is inevitable.

A more modest change from 7 oz. to 8 oz. gains only 4 yards even if the tempo of the swing is maintained.

The story is not complete unless the change in muscular effort entailed in swinging clubheads of different weights at the same speed is exhibited as well as the change in yardage shown in Fig. 13. This change of effort is shown in Fig. 14 where the effort used to swing a 7 oz. head is taken as the 100% datum. It is seen that the muscular effort is directly proportional to the weight of head.

Bear in mind that the clubhead speed is identical for all the head weights in the range. You can see at a glance how much effort you save by reducing head weight and how much extra you need to swing the heavier heads. Thus, the 5 oz. head needs only 71% of the effort required for the 7 oz., so that 29% is saved. Yet if you look at Fig. 13 the loss of distance is very much less in proportion, for 29% of effort is saved at a cost of 8% in distance. Similarly one ounce taken off the 7 oz. head saves 14% effort at the cost of 3% in distance.

Remarkable though the saving in effort is when weight is removed from the 7 oz. head (which is a fair average weight and our basis of comparison), the waste of effort following an increase in weight beyond 7 oz. is even more remarkable. For example, Fig. 14 shows that replacing the

7 oz. head by a 10 oz. head requires 44% extra effort to swing it at the same speed, but the gain in length, as shown in Fig. 13 is only 5.5% or 11 yards in 200. The extra effort is obviously out of all proportion to the extra distance.

The shaded areas in Figs. 13 and 14 enable you to see at glance how small are the changes in distance produced by large changes in muscular effort when clubhead weights are either reduced below or increased beyond the 7 oz. datum.

Clearly, while there is no point in going beyond 7 oz. there is much to be said for weight reduction. Consider for example the effect of changing from 7 oz. to 6 oz. The drop in distance is only 3% for the same speed of swing. But there is then a saving of 14% in muscular effort, and if that reserve of effort is utilised to swing the lighter head faster, it is easily proved that the net result is to gain 5% in distance, or 10 yards in 200.

Dropping the head weight to 5.5 oz gives a net gain in distance of 7% or 14 yards in 200. On the same basis a 5 oz. head gains 10% distance over a 7 oz. head or 20 yards in 200.

It is to be remembered, however, that to achieve these gains all parts of the body have to be moved faster although the pull applied to the club is the same. Thus, to obtain the 7% gain in distance through dropping the weight of head from 7 oz. to 5.5 oz., the motion of both body and club has to be 13% faster. For the club that is easy, since the necessary reserve effort of 21% (shown in Fig. 14) is there for that purpose. That does not cater for the body which has to find its own reserves to move 13% faster. It is therefore reassuring for the average player to know that moving the body that much faster is perfectly feasible because good players consistently swing 30% faster than the 200 yard man.

At the present time clubs with heads as light as 5 oz. are not on sale in the shops and that will probably remain true so long as the problem of designing suitable shafts for them is unsolved. For lighter heads demand lighter shafts (as is assumed in the above discussion). To design such shafts without sacrificing stiffness or satisfactory impact characteristics demands an advanced knowledge of structural vibration theory never so far applied to the design of golf clubs.

CHAPTER X

HOW CLUB LENGTH AND WEIGHT DISTRIBUTION AFFECTS THE SWING

It will be shown in Chapter XI that shaft flexibility has no influence on the swinging characteristics of a club. We are therefore left with only two properties which do have such influence, namely the overall weight and the way that weight is distributed. In general the head accounts for about half the weight and the shaft for the other half. The shaft tapers in diameter and also in weight from the grip to the head, though the precise way in which the weight tapers varies from one club to the next and can be affected by such factors as type of grip.

When a club is swung, every element of weight in the shaft is swung as well as the clubhead and the feel of the swing therefore depends not only on the weight of the head but also on the distribution of weight along the shaft.

Now it is easily proved that the net effect of all the elements of weight in head and shaft is exactly equivalent to a single concentrated weight situated some distance short of the head. If the clubhead is heavy and the shaft light this concentrated weight is pretty close to the clubhead - it would of course be coincident with the head if the shaft weighed nothing. For an average driver with say a 7 oz. head and weighing 13.5 oz. overall, this concentrated weight is located some 5 or 6 inches short of the head and weighs about 11 oz. A player swinging such a driver is actually swinging for all practical purposes a 11 oz. weight on a weightless shaft some 5 to 6 inches shorter than the actual shaft.

The important point to note is that everything that needs to be known about a club's swinging qualities - the 'feel' of the swing if you like - is completely defined by the weight of this concentrated mass and its distance from the hands. Its distance from the hands depends of course on where the hands hold the club. A reasonable point to take for this purpose is some 4 inches from the extreme end of the shaft. Having assumed this, one can very easily find the distance of the concentrated mass from this point. A quick and very direct way is as follows. Tie a small weight to the end of a piece of thread of about the same length as the shaft. Now hold the club by finger and thumb 4 inches from the end, letting the clubhead hang like a pendulum, with the other hand hold the thread on which the weight hangs and bring the two hands close together with shaft and thread hanging parallel. Start both of them gently oscillating. If you start off with the weight level with the clubhead the latter will swing faster. Gradually shorten the thread till clubhead and weight swing in step for at least ten oscillations. The length of the thread is then equal to the distance of the concentrated weight from the hands. It is in fact the length of the equivalent simple pendulum.

An alternative and more accurate method is to count the number of complete oscillations which the clubhead makes in 60 seconds with the club held by finger and thumb in the way described above. The time for one oscillation is then found by dividing the 60 seconds by the number of oscillations. Suppose it is T seconds. The length required is then $9.76T^2$.

For a particular driver oscillated in this way the time T for one oscillation was 1.87 secs, so that the length required was $9.76 \times (1.87)^2$ or 34 inches. If the distance from hands to clubhead is 39 inches this means that the concentrated weight is 5 inches short of the clubhead.

Having found the distance of the concentrated mass we can find its weight very easily. Suppose for the driver just mentioned the distance of the centre of gravity (i.e. point of balance) of the club from the hands is 25 inches. The required weight is then 25/34 (i.e. 25 divided by the pendulum length) of the total weight of the club i.e. 25/34 of 13.5 oz. or 10 oz.

If you have a favourite club and want to be able to replace it with a club with the same swing characteristics, make sure that you know the 'vital statistics' of your own club - pendulum length and pendulum weight. You have then a solid scientific basis for choosing a replacement should the occasion arise.

In what follows the concentrated weight will be referred to as the 'pendulum weight' and its distance from the hands as the 'pendulum length'.

How the pendulum length of a club affects the swing

The effect of changing the weight of a club on the distance to which the ball can be hit has already been discussed in a previous chapter. As there explained, the only effect of changing the weight of a club, so long as head and shaft are changed in proportion, is to change the tempo of the swing. The swing itself, i.e. the sequence of positions through which the hands and club pass are not affected by change of weight; a heavier club means a slower swing and vice versa, that is all.

This is true only if head and shaft (including grip) are changed in proportion, for then the pendulum length is unaffected despite changes in the pendulum weight. Any change in weight that is not strictly in proportion, however, causes a change in the pendulum length and has an effect on the swing itself apart from its tempo. Thus lightening the shaft by replacing steel by aluminium lengthens the pendulum length unless the clubhead is lightened in the same proportion.

Where the change in the pendulum length is no more than an inch or two the effect on the swing is not noticeable. In any set of clubs the difference between the pendulum lengths of the four wooden clubs is negligibly small, but the shorter lengths of the iron have a distinct effect on the timing.

The effect of changing the length of a clubshaft on the timing of the swing is made clear by the mathematical analysis, and what that shows explains what previously was known only from trial and error methods.

One thing that becomes clear is that one must take account of length of arms when discussing clubshaft length. When I say length of arms I mean the distance or radius between the hands and the centre of rotation round which they swing, and the longer the arms the longer is that radius. For players of average build the radius of the arc along which the hands move is about 2 ft. and the average length of a driver, let us say, is 42 inches or 3.5 ft.

Suppose now this player of average bulld were to add 6 inches to his 42 in. driver, so changing the length from 3.5 ft to 4 ft., i.e. by 14%. What is true is that, if the player could at the same time increase the length of his arms also by 14%, his timing would be unaffected. By timing I mean that his wrists would start to uncock at the same stage in the downswing as before and the sequence of positions passed through in the course of the swing would be unaltered. The clubhead, now moving over a wider orbit, would of course move 14% faster (and require 30% more effort) if the swing was performed in the same time. In other words he could afford to slow down his swing by 14% and still have the same clubhead speed (and the same effort) as before the change in length was made.

As it is, however, a man's length of arm is not adjustable, and the real question is 'Just how is a player's swing affected by adding 6 in. to the length of his driver? To appreciate the answer to this question let me refer you back to Fig. 2. You will remember my explaining that during the first, or one-piece stage of the downswing, during which the hands moved from A to B and the clubhead from D to E, the wrists remain fully cocked. But that from B to C - the second or power stage - the wrists were progressively uncocked *by centrifugal force* so as to bring clubshaft and arms into line at impact.

Now the crux of the matter is that the more the clubshaft is lengthened the earlier must the uncocking of the wrists start, i.e. the farther up the arc must the point B be located. This is because the centrifugal force takes longer to bring the clubhead into line with the hands as the shaft is lengthened. It is as if the centrifugal force addressed the player in the following terms. 'If you want me to make this lengthened club of yours catch up with the hands at impact, you must allow me to start the chase earlier, for point B is now too late in the swing to start. And if you say that this will unduly encroach on the first stage of the arc (from B to A) then you will either have to push the starting point A further back or use more effort so as to pack more acceleration into the shortened arc.'

That really summarises the situation. It means that the amount by which a club can be lengthened no matter how light it is made is severely restricted, for a point is soon reached where the necessary length of arc for the centrifugal force to do its snapping-into-line job is just not available.

Let me disabuse you of the fallacy that using a lighter clubhead in conjunction with the lengthened shaft will help the centrifugal force to bring the clubhead into line with the hands earlier. It will not, and for the very simple reason that reducing the weight of the clubhead reduces the centrifugal force in the same proportion. This means that the limiting length of shaft that can be conveniently used is independent of weight. A one ounce head, for example, at the end of a weightless 6 ft. shaft cannot be brought into line with the hands at impact through the agency of centrifugal force without ruining the timing. This is merely another way of saying that a long club however light is not amenable to flail action. Unless of course the player's arms could be lengthened in the same proportion!

It is clear from what has been said above that a short-armed player with a 43 inch club is already using a club that is too long for him, and it would be the height of folly for him to go in for a still longer club under the mistaken idea of making up by club length what he lacks in length of arms. What he should undoubtedly do is to use a club shorter and lighter than standard - most certainly lighter.

CHAPTER XI

CLUBSHAFT FLEXIBILITY

Although the subject of clubshaft flexibility or whippiness is a perennial source of discussion and argument in the golfing press, the fact remains that no more is known about it at the present time than was known twenty or thirty years ago. There is a persistent idea that elderly players stand to gain distance by a change to more whippy shafts. Every so often one reads a letter from an elderly golfer complaining of loss of distance with advancing years and querying the advisability of a change to more whippy clubs. Almost invariably the reply from the oracle responsible for replying to correspondents' letters is in the affirmative. The oracle, usually a well-known professional, has probably never tried whippy clubs himself and therefore has no real basis for the advice he gives.

Two factors perhaps explain his response. For one thing, there is a traditional idea, mistaken though it is, that a more flexible shaft can be of help in such cases. For another, and perhaps just as strong a factor, he senses that the writer of the letter wants to be told to try the more flexible clubshafts. It is something to pin his hopes on. Brutally to be told that changing clubs would be money down the drain and that there is no way of cheating 'anno domini' would be to dash those hopes to the ground and create despondency. On every count therefore there is a strong incentive to advocate the change.

Now the purpose of this chapter is to prove as a fact of mechanics that nothing can possibly be gained by resorting to flexible shafts. I realise that such a proof must be one hundred per cent convincing if it is to overthrow a belief that has become enshrined in the traditions of the game. So securely enshrined indeed is this belief that it has become the main basis for the classification of clubs. There are at present six grades of shafts in Britain: 'X' for very stiff, 'S' for stiff, 'R' for regular, 'A' for flexible, 'L' for ladies, and 'W' for whippy ladies - all equally meaningless so far as they affect performance. But let us get on with the proof.

There are three equally convincing independent reasons why a change in shaft flexibility can be of no benefit, and each of the three constitutes a hundred per cent proof.

Let us first be clear how the advocates of flexible shafts *think* they can be of benefit. Their argument is - and as far as I can see there cannot be any other - that a flexible shaft, bent backwards at an earlier stage in the downswing, is in the process of 'swishing' forward again at impact, thus imparting additional velocity to the clubhead. In other words, the elastic energy stored in the bent shaft earlier on is released as kinetic energy at impact.

First proof

Have now a good look at the multi-flash photograph of Fig. 1, or, if you like, at any of the hundreds of action photographs that are available in books and periodicals. Better still, perhaps, look at the way your own clubhead is set if you stop your swing half-way down. In every case the *heel of the clubhead is leading* all the way down to within a couple of feet of the ball. Any bending action applied to the club must therefore take place while the heel is leading. And this means that the bend in the shaft is in the direction heel-to-nose, i.e. parallel to the face. It means further that any spring-back must also be parallel to the face. But a spring-back parallel to the face is not what is wanted. What is wanted is a spring-back in a direction perpendicular to the face, i.e. in the direction the ball will travel. As there is no spring-back in that direction there cannot be any extra clubhead speed either.

This should be conclusive proof to any layman since it depends on nothing more than everyday experience and plain common sense. However, let us proceed to the second proof.

Second proof

Forget now the fact that the shaft bends in the wrong plane and let us see whether, in the absence of that damaging fact, there would be a possibility of deriving some advantage from a flexible shaft.

In previous chapters I have pointed out that hand leverage, which alone can cause the shaft to bend, takes place only in the first stage of the downswing and is of no account in the second stage. It is worthwhile here to examine the photograph of Fig. 1 again in order to see where and when the shaft does bend. I think you will agree that the bend - a backward bend - is most pronounced when the left arm is about horizontal, i.e. at the 10th exposure counting backwards from the ball. You will further notice that the bend has disappeared and the shaft has recovered its straightness in a further four exposures, i.e. by the time the shaft has reached the horizontal. But everyone knows that, whether you are handling a cane or a fishing rod, the 'swishing' speed of its tip is greatest when it is passing through the straight position from a previously bent position. But the shaft in the picture has recovered its straightness by the time it is horizontal and this therefore is where the 'swishing' velocity is a maximum - five exposures from the impact position (counting back from the ball). It follows that any extra speed that might be gained from the spring-back of the shaft takes place far too early. In fact, since there is 1/100 sec. between two successive exposures, the shaft springs back to the straight in 4/100 sec. when there is still more than another 4/100 sec. before impact takes place.

Of course if spring-back time were 8/100 sec., instead of 4/100 sec. the shaft would straighten at about the time of impact. But, and *this is the important point*, to bring that about the shaft would have to be at least 4 times as flexible. Such a degree of flexibility, however, is out of the question and more appropriate to a fishing rod than a golf club. It means that a shaft held horizontally at the grip would dip some 4 inches under a 1 lb. weight hung at the head instead of the 1 inch dip of the average shaft.

It becomes clear therefore that, even in the most favourable conditions, a shaft would need to have a completely unacceptable degree of whippiness to confer any benefit from its 'swishing' action. Here therefore is a second convincing argument against the idea that anything can be gained by monkeying about with shaft flexibility.

Third proof

It is hardly necessary to pile proof on proof, so I will only mention that it is easy to calculate on the basis of vibration theory that, even if the disabilities mentioned above did not exist, any extra clubhead speed derived from the swishing action of a whippy shaft is in any case a mere bagatelle, certainly no more than 2%, i.e. 4 yards in a 200 yard drive.

What has been said above demolishes once and for all the basis for grading clubs according to shaft stiffness. The sooner therefore manufacturers abandon the rigmarole of the six stiffness gradings at present in vogue the better (and cheaper) for all concerned. Simple pendulum length and weight as described in Chapter X are the only valid basis for grading clubs. Stiffness enters the question only in so far as it is necessary to have a modicum of flexibility to prevent damage by inadvertently hitting the ground. A shaft must also be stiff enough to give no hint of floppiness, which is the reason why first-class players insist on stiffness combined with lightness.

One further point needs to be made here and it is an important one. It has to do with the fact that when a manufacturer makes a shaft more flexible he also 'ipso facto' makes it lighter. Now benefit *can* accrue from making a shaft lighter, and therefore it is pretty certain that players who swear to getting better results with a more flexible shaft owe them not to increased flexibility but to increased lightness. It is possible to make a shaft lighter without increasing its flexibility and that is the goal to aim at.

The reader may think that, since incontrovertible proof has now been given that there is no sense in grading clubs according to shaft stiffness, manufacturers will abandon the practice and give up the pretence that there is a degree of stiffness to suit each class of player. They will not. The only thing that will make them change their practice is a change in demand. Once the ordinary golfer is convinced - and what has been said above should convince him - that grading clubs by shaft stiffness is meaningless, the manufacturer will eventually come into line.

You, the reader of this chapter, may have seen the recently published book entitled 'In search of the perfect golf swing' to which I have occasion to refer in the next chapter. If so, I think it only fair to you that I should explain why the views expressed in that book on the present subject are in error. It is essential that I do as otherwise you might be tempted to doubt the correctness of what I have said in this chapter on the subject of flexible shafts.

In the next chapter I explain, in a way which you will find conclusive, how the authors of the book in question have mis-interpreted the pre-impact forward bend of the clubshaft, which is such a noticeable feature of all action photographs of players, especially when swinging wood clubs. They have attributed this forward bend to a forward springing action of the shaft from a backward bend induced earlier in the downswing, in other words, to a vibratory movement of the shaft.

In point of fact, as explained in Chapter XII, the observed forward bend of the shaft of wood clubs is caused by something quite different, namely the gradual build-up of the centrifugal force at the clubhead as it approaches the point of impact. This force acts along the straight line connecting the hands to the (centre of gravity) of the clubhead as shown in Fig. 15(a) and causes the shaft to bend as shown in Fig. 15(b). Furthermore, because the centre of gravity (c.g.) of the clubhead is well behind the line of the shaft in all wood clubs, the shaft bends not only upward as in Fig. 15(b) but also at the same time forward as in Fig. 15(d).

To see for yourself how the kind of bend shown in Fig. 15(b) is produced by a pulling action between the centre of gravity of the head at G and the hands at B, place your heel on the grounded clubhead of any wood club and apply a plain pull to the other end of the shaft. You will note how the shaft bows upward as a result. If you place your heel well back of the line of the shaft to simulate a rearward centre of gravity (and used your other foot to stop the head sliding sideways) you will note how the same pull produces a forward as well as an upward bend in the shaft, i.e. *a bend perpendicular to the face as well as parallel to the face.*

It is most interesting to follow the bending behaviour of the shaft right through the downswing. Turn therefore again to the multi-flash picture of Bobby Jones's swing in Fig. 1. For several exposures at the start the shaft remains straight but by the time the clubhead has reached a point behind the left shoulder the shaft has already begun to bend backward in the plane of the face. At exposure 10 (counting back from the ball) this kind of bend reaches its maximum value. It is due to the leverage applied by the wrists in the first stage of the downswing, and when that leverage disappears in the second stage the bending it induces also disappears. The result is that at exposure 6 the shaft is dead straight. In exposure 5 you see the *bending effect of the centrifugal pull beginning to appear.* As explained already this causes the shaft to bend both parallel to the face and perpendicular to the face. It is the bend parallel to the face that is beginning to appear in exposure 5 because any bend perpendicular to the face cannot in that position of the shaft be observed since it is in the line of vision. However, as the face gradually turns over preparatory to becoming square to the ball at impact, you can see more of the bend perpendicular to the face and less of the other. In exposure 1, the last before impact, only the bend perpendicular to the face (that shown in Fig. 15(d)) can be seen since the upward bend parallel to the face is now invisible.

Impact with the ball gives the clubhead a backward smack which is violent enough to change the pre-impact forward bend into a post-impact backward bend. This sudden backward bend and the very quick straightening out that follows in the very next exposure has already been fully discussed in Chapter VI. All the vibratory movement excited by the impact has completely died out by the time that exposure 8 (after impact) is reached, and you will note that thereafter the characteristic bend (a nose-ward bowing) due to centrifugal force reasserts itself despite the slowing down of the head. The bend perpendicular to the face is also present but cannot be seen because it is in the line of vision.

Every aspect of the bending behaviour of the shaft is thus fully accounted for. For the first time in the history of the game, the peculiar bending behaviour of clubshafts, as the impact point is approached, is given a scientific explanation - an explanation moreover which effectively disposes of the idea that any kind of springy vibration is involved.

Changes in loft and toe-in of the club resulting from the action of centrifugal force are dealt with in the next chapter. What I want to emphasise here - indeed to ram home - is that *no possible advantage can accrue in the way of added clubhead velocity from the use of whippy shafts.* They are a snare and delusion, and it is a great pity that front-rank professionals should lend their authority to perpetuating that delusion. They might be excused if they themselves turned to flexible shafts to obtain added distance. They do not, yet, with no personal experience nor indeed any knowledge of the matter in question, they have the temerity to broadcast their ill-considered advice to the elderly golfer and to women. What I have said here will I trust, settle the question once and for all.

To conclude this chapter I am going to show you how in a matter of minutes you can convince yourself that no possible benefit can be obtained from shaft flexibility. I shall do so, not by appealing to your reasoning powers as I have done already in this chapter, nor by pointing out the difficulty of timing a vibrating shaft in the downswing, but by the simple expedient of showing that *no vibration takes place at all.*

Here is the test. Place eight inches of the butt end of a driver on the edge of a table with the head and the rest of the shaft unsupported and projecting horizontally from the table edge. Press down hard on the butt end with your right hand and give the head a downward tap with the left. You will notice that the head will continue to vibrate up and down many times before the vibration finally dies away. This of course is the vibration which everyone, including the best known golf club manufacturers, imagine is set up in the downswing.

Now to convince yourself that in actual fact no such vibration does take place during the downswing following the initial bending back which is a feature of the first stage of the downswing.

Hold the same club now in your two hands as you would in preparing to swing it. Place the face of the clubhead against some fixed object such as the arm of a settee and apply leverage with the hands so as to produce a distinct bend in the shaft to represent the way it bends in the initial part of the downswing. If the head is in contact with the extreme edge of the settee arm you can now let the head suddenly slip forward in the direction your hands are pressing it. As it slips do not try to stop its motion but let it move forward freely. Note carefully however what happens to the shaft and the head. The shaft immediately straightens *but does not vibrate.*

That is the crux of the whole matter. *The shaft straightens but does so not on its way to springing forward again but to remain straight.* The vibration, in other words, is nipped in the bud.

This immediate and total smothering of the vibration is due to what the engineer would call the 'damping' action of the hands. In the downswing the release from the initial bend is not so sudden and therefore the smothering action is then even more effective.

I do not need to tell you after you have made this simple test that anyone who considers the pre-impact vibration of shafts as a factor in design is barking up the wrong tree and is wasting his time.

CHAPTER XII

WHY CLUBS HAVE A LOFT AND A TOE-IN AT IMPACT DIFFERENT FROM THEIR NOMINAL VALUES

I t will come as a surprise to players and club-makers alike to know that the nominal loft and toe-in of their clubs are not those that operate at impact with the ball. It has never been realised by club-makers that the action of centrifugal force on the clubhead at impact increases the loft of all wood clubs to such an extent as to convert a driver into a near brassie and a brassie into a near spoon. Neither have they yet realised that the same centrifugal force causes the shaft to take up enough of a forward bend just before impact to introduce a toe-in of the face of anything between two and three degrees of angle.

These changes in loft and toe-in are the result of shaft flexibility, and would not occur if the clubshaft were dead rigid. For conventional shafts, however, even the stiffest at present in use, they are changes that are far from negligible.

You may wonder how it is that the centrifugal pull on the clubhead can bend a shaft so as to produce the changes above noted. A few simple diagrams will make the situation crystal clear.

In Fig. 15 I have purposely exaggerated the situation by extending the heel-to-nose length of the clubhead and shortening the shaft. Fig. 15(a) represents the club in the impact position; AB is the shaft, AC the clubhead and B the hands, while G marks the c.g. (centre of gravity) of the clubhead. The centrifugal force acting on the clubhead must of course pass through its c.g. and also through the hands which resist that force. The line of action of the opposing forces F is therefore along the dotted line AB.

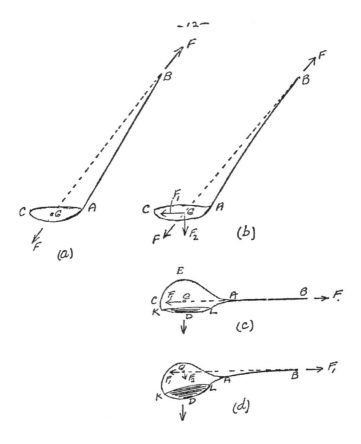

Fig. 15. How bending of shaft by centrifugal force produces
toe-in of clubhead and increases loft

It is clear that under such opposing forces there is a tendency to straighten out the angle at A between the shaft and the clubhead with the result that the shaft bends in the way shown in Fig 15(b). You can satisfy yourself in a few seconds that the shaft does bend in the way illustrated. Take a wood club and place your right heel on the grounded head. Now apply a pull with the hands to the grip end and note the bowing of the shaft.

You can learn something else from this, and that is that the bowing produced by a moderate pull is not much less pronounced than what a much fiercer pull can produce. This is why the amount of loft and toe-in is only a little greater in a powerful swing than it is in a swing of less power. If you try to stretch a weighted horizontal string you will appreciate the reason, because the dip in the string is reduced only a little when you double the pull - it is certainly not halved.

You can now understand the connection between centrifugal force and bending of the shaft. To see the further connection between bending of the shaft and gain in loft and toe-in, you need to look at Fig. 15 (c) and Fig. 15 (d). Fig. 15 (c) is the plan view of Fig. 15 (b), i.e. it represents what you see when looking at Fig. 15 (b) from above. You therefore see the crown (ACE) of the clubhead and a foreshortened view KDL of its face.

If now the centre of gravity of the clubhead at G is in line with - or rather in the same vertical plane as - the shaft in the address position, the bowing of the shaft shown in (b) will be an upward bowing when looked at from above. Which means that no appreciable change, either in loft or in toe-in takes place as a result of the shaft bending under the straightening influence of the forces F.

Suppose, however that the centre of gravity is not in line with the shaft but well behind it as at G_1 in Fig 15. (d). The centrifugal force F as always, acts along the straight line joining the hands to the centre of gravity of the head i.e. along the dotted line BG_1. And, just as in the elevation view there was a tendency to straighten out the angle GAB at A in the vertical plane, so in the plan view Fig. 15 (d) there is a tendency to straighten out the angle GAB at A in the horizontal plane. The result is again to bend the shaft AB, but this time not upward but forward as shown. Such a forward bend produces a toe-in effect as is clearly indicated in view Fig. 15 (d).

If you consider the elevation view again Fig. 15 (b), you will understand that the resultant centrifugal force F can be just as well represented by its two components F_1 and F_2 as there indicated. It is the component FE that produces the bend in the shaft in view (d). The other component F_2 cannot be shown in that view because it is directed downward through the paper. Imagine therefore the effect of a pushing-down force F_2 at G in the plan view Fig 15. (d). Such a down push, being offset from the clubhead support at A tends clearly to depress the back part E of the head and raise the front, with the result that more of the clubface - shown shaded - becomes visible. Thus, there is a slight skyward rotation of the face compared with its angle in view Fig. 15. (c), in other words, an increase in loft.

I have gone into this bit of geometry primarily for the edification of golf-club manufacturers and their technical advisers, as it is high time that they should be made aware of this particular phenomenon and have its undesirable effects eliminated from future designs. This offers no real difficulty, since all that needs doing is to have the weight of the clubhead so distributed as to bring its centre of gravity into line with the shaft at address.

There is a simple way to check whether this has been accomplished. Just balance the shaft horizontally on the forefinger of the left hand, with the clubhead facing forward (nose pointing down) and the shaft passing close to the right hip. Looking down on the clubhead you get a view like that shown in Fig. 16(a) in which the profile AB of the baseplate ABC slopes down to the left, with the clubface well exposed. Now give the shaft a slight clockwise rotation with the right hand to bring the base-plate profile AB square with the shaft and bring the edge of the face into the line of vision as in Fig. 16(b). If you take away your right hand, the clubhead will flop back into position again, because the centre of gravity of the head is to the left of the centre line LL of the shaft - largely because the lead weight is located well to the rear of the head.

What is required is either to shift the position of the lead weight or to shift the position of the shaft relative to the head in such a way as to make the clubhead *balance in position* Fig. 16(b). The centre of gravity of the head will then be in the same vertical plane as the shaft when the club is grounded in the address position.

As a result, the pre-impact bend in the clubshaft, at present a distinctive and universally observed feature of all wood clubs, will be eliminated, together with its undesirable consequences - the increased loft and the built-in draw. Note that all this applies only to wood clubs. All iron clubs have the centre of gravity of the head much more in line with the shaft, so that when the shaft bows as in Fig. 15(b) the bow is mostly in line with the face and therefore affects loft and toe-in to a much more limited extent. Another factor, however, affects the angular setting of the blades of iron clubs and this will be discussed at the end of this chapter.

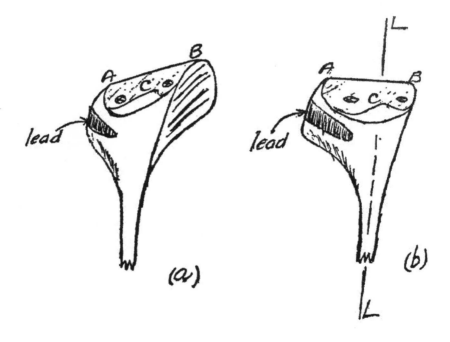

Fig 16. Set of clubhead when (a) unbalanced and (b) balanced
with club supported at its centre of gravity

Although this pre-impact bend of wood clubs has not gone unnoticed in the past, the reason for it has never before been explained. It has always been thought to be due to shaft vibration - the shaft springing forward after being sprung back at an earlier stage in the downswing. This interpretation is largely responsible for the still prevalent notion that a clubshaft can be made to act as a spring to give added velocity in a direction perpendicular to the face i.e. in the direction of travel of the clubhead at impact. This view, unfortunately, has been given renewed currency in a recently published book* which the authors mistakenly attribute the characteristic pre-impact bending of the clubshaft above described to a forward-springing action of the shaft. For, in referring to the pre-impact forward bend of the shaft, they state that the clubhead 'has already <u>sprung forward</u> to the limit of its travel by the time it strikes the ball' (my underlining).

The fact is - and I say this quite categorically - that *at no stage in the downswing, right up to impact; does the clubshaft vibrate in the direction in which the face points* (i.e. perpendicular to the face). Since no such vibration can be set up, no added velocity of the clubhead can be generated - a point already emphasised in Chapter XI. There is no question of timing that type of vibration in order to benefit from it, as suggested by the authors of the book above referred to, because *one cannot time a swing to suit a vibration that does not exist.*

The sequence of events, so far as bending of the shaft in the course of the downswing is concerned, can be described in a few simple words. In the first stage of the downswing the shaft bends back *in the plane of the face* alone, therefore no clubhead vibration is generated in the direction the face points to. The shaft then quickly springs back to the straight before the shaft has dropped to the horizontal, and the vibration - if it can be called a vibration, when only half an oscillation has taken place - dies out, smothered by the damping action of the hands. For the remainder of the downswing right up to impact, the only bending that takes place is that due to the centrifugal pull of the clubhead described above - a quasi-static and not a vibrating kind of bend and incapable of

---

* *'The search for the perfect swing', by A. Cochran and J. Stobbs (Heinemann Press, 1968).*

increasing the velocity of the head. The impact with the ball of course sets up a post-impact vibration of the shaft and that *does* cause the head to oscillate in the direction the face points as is fully described in Chapter VII. It is the only time in the downswing and follow-through that such a type of vibration takes place.

The way the above description tallies with the behaviour of the shaft as shown in the multiflash picture of Bobby Jones's swing in Fig. 1 has already been described in Chapter XI.

I mentioned earlier that there is a factor which affects iron clubs in a way that wood clubs are not affected, or at least not affected to any appreciable extent. Two properties of iron clubs account for this difference:-

(i)   iron clubs have the centre of gravity of the head in line with the shaft at address

(ii) iron clubs have a greater loft than wood clubs.

By virtue of property (i) the shaft of an iron club bows vertically upwards due to the action of centrifugal force as the point of impact is approached. Such upward bowing would have no effect, either on the loft or on the toe-heel angle (i.e. the amount of toe-in or toe-out) of the clubhead, if the striking face had no loft. It is therefore the presence of loft that affects the angular setting of the face of an iron club. What happens is that *the original or designed loft remains unchanged but that the toe-heel angle is changed so as to introduce a toe-out effect.* The amount of toe-out depends on the length and flexibility of the clubshaft, on the velocity of the clubhead (since that determines the centrifugal force), on the weight of the clubhead and the distance its centre of gravity is offset from the line of the shaft. Principally, however, the amount of toe-out is determined by the loft of the club.

To give you an idea of the amount of toe-out involved, a No. 2 iron has a toe-out of about 1.5° whereas a No. 8 iron which has a little more than twice the loft has a toe-out of about 3°.

What is important is that every single iron in your bag has a built-in fade, just as every wood club has a built-in draw. And this at once suggests the cure. For the toe-in effect in wood clubs is caused by having the centre of gravity well behind the line of the shaft. Why not therefore design iron clubs to have the centre of gravity a little behind the line of the shaft instead of as at present, dead in line? The required amount will vary with the loft of the club - increasing with increased loft - but in each case it will be designed to cancel out the existing toe-out.

Effect of increased slope of shaft at impact compared with slope at address

There is another factor which accentuates the effect just described. This is the fact that at impact the slope of the clubshaft is invariably greater than that at address. It is the result of the hands, due to the centrifugal pull, being slightly higher at impact than at address, as Fig. 8 (a), (b) and (c) clearly shows. The increase in slope amounts to about three degrees and has the same kind of effect on the angular setting of the blade of an iron club as that produced by bowing of the shaft. In the case of a No. 5 iron it adds another 1.5° to the 2° already present due to the bowing of the shaft. These figures are only approximate but it can be confidently stated that the resultant effect for the more lofted iron clubs is to introduce a toe-out of at least 3° and a distinct tendency to fade the ball.

If you are a little sceptical about the above statement and are somewhat mystified as to how a lift of the hands in the address position can cause an effective toe-out, you can convince yourself of its truth in a very simple way. Take the most lofted club in your bag – a sand iron for preference - and take up your usual address position with it. While keeping the clubhead grounded, lift up your hands a few inches thus increasing the slope of the shaft and tilting the clubhead forward in line with it. You will note that whereas the face of the blade was pointed towards the (imaginary) hole before, it is now pointing outward and partly at right angles to the previous direction, thus producing a toe-out effect. If you perform the same test with a zero-lift putter, a lift of the hands now merely makes the nose drop relative to the heel, while leaving the direction in which the blade faces unchanged - still squarely facing the hole. It thus becomes clear why the effective toe-out increases with the loft of the club.

What I have described in this chapter is something that has never been appreciated by club manufacturers. Not that the geometry involved is other than elementary. What they and everyone else have been blind to is the change in the angular setting of the club face due to the shaft-bending effect of the strong centrifugal force to which the clubhead is subjected during the pre-impact stage of the swing.

As already indicated, the consequent disabilities inherent in present-day club design can easily be countered by suitable design changes and I cannot imagine that it will be long before club manufacturers take advantage of them.

That the effects of the changes in the angular settings of club faces have not been noticed in play can only be attributed to the fact that they are, after all, fairly small and that in any case top-class players must by this time have subconsciously so conditioned their technique as to counter them. This however is hardly a convincing argument for allowing these faults in club design to persist.

CHAPTER XIII

SOME FACTS ABOUT THE GOLF BALL

Back in 1958 Lord Brabazon was concerned with the U.S.G.A. in finding some method by which to limit the distances that long-hitting players can send the modern golf ball, and so in turn limiting the length of golf courses and reducing the times and distances involved in playing them. At his instigation and in conjunction with the Dunlop Sports Company I became involved in the problem. The first possibility explored was to increase the aerodynamic drag of the ball by modifying the surface pattern in some way. To do this it was necessary to consider, in the light of previous experimental and theoretical aerodynamical research on the drag of spheres, why the present pattern had been adopted.

Experiments carried out by Dunlop's had shown that there was an optimum depth of indentations that produced maximum distance. This gave a quantitative value to what was previously known only qualitatively from theory and experiment. It was known that the type of airflow over a smooth sphere is quite different from that over a sphere with a roughened surface, in that the turbulent wake created by a smooth sphere, contrary to what might be expected, is wider than that created by a roughened sphere and therefore causes greater drag. This however, is only true up to a certain critical speed at which the drag on a smooth sphere suffers a sudden drop to about a fifth of its previous value. That critical speed is in the region of the speed with which a ball leaves the tee from a hard drive, and therefore a hard hitter would stand to benefit from the sudden drop in drag were it not for a rather strange characteristic of the smooth ball. This is the peculiar way in which it responds to spin.

A point on the equator of a spinning golf ball in flight has a resultant speed that is made up of two components - the speed of travel of the centre of the ball through the air and the speed at the equator due to spin. They may be referred to as the flight speed and the equatorial speed. If an ordinary golf ball is hit with side-spin, everyone knows that if it spins in clockwise direction (looking down on it) the left side is under heavier air pressure than the right and the ball therefore veers away to the right in a slice. Similarly, if it is hit with back spin, the under side is the one under the heavier pressure and the ball rises.

In the case of the smooth ball, however, the way in which it curves in the air depends on the ratio between the flight speed and the equatorial speed. If the ratio (equatorial speed)/(flight speed) is less than 1/3, i.e. if the spin is deficient a sliced ball will start with a hook and finish with a slice and a hooked ball will start with a slice and finish with a hook. Correspondingly a ball given back spin starts by dipping and finally rises - if it does not hit the ground first. For drives and other distance shots the spin on the ball is never strong enough to avoid this sort of erratic flight.

These peculiarities of the smooth ball were not understood in the early days and all that players knew was that a smooth ball behaved in an erratic way. The idea of dimpling the surface of the ball in order to achieve better flight characteristics came about by accident. It was noticed that a ball roughened by wear had a steadier and longer flight than a ball and players soon adopted the practice of deliberately roughening balls to improve their trajectory. Manufacturers eventually cottoned on to the idea and so the dimpled ball was born.

Subsequent investigation has shown that the drop in air drag that takes place suddenly and at a certain critical speed in the case of the smooth ball takes place gradually for the dimpled ball and over a wide range of speeds right up to the highest attainable in practice. I have shown elsewhere[*] that, as a result of this, the drag of a golf ball is proportional to

---

[*]   D. Williams 'Drag on a golf ball in flight and its practical significance'.
      Quart. Journal of Mechanics and Applied Maths. August, 1959.

its speed and not to the square of its speed. In consequence, the distance (carry) of a golf ball is almost directly proportional to its starting speed.

It may be of interest here to reproduce a table that appeared in an article by Mr. S. G. Ball of the Dunlop Company in 'Golfing'* for February 1952. This shows how the 'carry' and total length of a drive vary with depth of indentation of the ball:

Depth of Pattern	Carry	Total Length of Drive
0.002 inches	117 yards	146 yards
0.004 inches	187 yards	212 yards
0.006 inches	212 yards	232 yards
0.008 inches	223 yards	238 yards
0.010 inches	238 yards	261 yards
0.012 inches	225 yards	240 yards

You will note from this how the 'carry' and the total length gradually increase with the depth of the pattern until an optimum depth of 0.01 inches is reached, beyond which it is clearly unprofitable to go.

What is of considerable interest here, in view of what was said above about the smooth ball, is the very small carry of the nearly smooth ball entered first in the table: it is only half that of the ball with the maximum carry and this is due without doubt to the quick-dipping flight caused by the back spin.

It becomes clear from the above remarks that the idea of limiting long drives by regulations governing the surface pattern of the ball is unworkable, quite apart from the question of enforcing any such regulations.

A far more feasible method of limiting the distances obtainable by long hitters is to reduce the weight of the ball without changing its size. Because, if there is no spin, the distance covered will be directly

---

*   Reproduced by kind permission of the editor of 'Golfing'.

proportional to the weight of the ball for the same starting speed. If, for example, the 1.62 oz. English ball were reduced in weight by 20% to 1.3 oz., one would expect a loss of 16% in length - so cutting down the 250 yard drive to 210 yard and the 200 yard drive to 170 yards.

Experiments carried out by Dunlop have shown that the effect of back spin is to reduce the loss of length by some 5%. Even so, it is almost certain that very few golfers would be prepared to sacrifice such a large percentage of the distance they have been used to obtaining, however substantial the economic advantages.

In point of fact the question will never arise because anyone who has tried playing with a 1.3 oz. ball (as I have by courtesy of Messrs. Dunlops) knows that every golfer would condemn it out of hand as being much too difficult to control. It is only after trying out such a ball that one realises what a good compromise the standard 1.62 oz. ball represents. A hard hit tee shot with a driver of 10° loft sends it climbing in almost a straight line, the weight of the ball being beautifully balanced by the aerodynamic lift due to the back spin. By contrast the lighter ball zooms up along a path of steepening slope under the effect of back spin and then floats along to reach a carry only some 10% shorter than the heavier ball. Because it lands more vertically than the heavier ball it loses about another 5% distance because of a shorter run after landing.

What puts it quite out of court, however, is its extreme sensitiveness to side spin. What would be a mild fade for the standard ball becomes a slice, just as a modest draw becomes a hook.

As to what degree of weight reduction golfers are prepared to stand for, some guide is provided by their attitude to the American-size ball. As everyone knows the larger American ball weighs the same (1.62 oz.) as the English ball but has a diameter of 1.68 in. against 1.62 in. It has therefore a frontal area 7% greater than the English ball and this has nearly the same effect as lightening the English ball by 7% to make it 1.5 oz. Such a ball, according to what has been said above, would give a slightly reduced distance and would be a little more sensitive to spin. This, indeed, is everyone's experience with the American ball.

It is interesting to know (from what was said to me by Mr. S. G. Ball of Dunlop) that a slightly lighter version of the American-size ball was actually standardised in America for about a year in January 1931. The lighter version weighed 1.55 oz. and therefore was 4.3% lighter than before. There was (according to Mr. Ball) 'an outcry from the general body of players' and the weight had to be put back to the original 1.62 oz.

This gives us a clue as to the degree of lightening that would be tolerated by golfers in general. For we have already seen that changing from the English to the American ball is almost equivalent to reducing the weight of the English ball by 7% to make it 1.5 oz. It appears therefore that a further reduction of 4.3% to bring it down to 1.44 would be unacceptable.

As to choosing between a change over to the American-size ball and making the nearly equivalent change of reducing the weight of the English ball to 1.5 oz., most players, one would think, would plump for the bigger ball. The loss of distance it entails can be made up by improving its elastic properties but its greater sensitiveness to spin, is something one has to accept and get used to. It goes without saying therefore that any player who has got used to controlling the American ball finds it easier to control the less spin-sensitive English ball. Conversely, players who have come to rely on the margin of error allowed by the English ball find the larger ball something of a handful. This is a handicap that British players have to face when playing in America.

Effect of ball elasticity

A quick way to get some idea of the relative elasticity or liveliness of two balls is to drop them together from the same height onto a hard floor - tile or concrete. The ball that bounces higher is the more elastic of the two *for that kind of gentle Impact*. I have emphasised the last phrase because the better ball in such a test may not be the better ball under the kind of violent blow it receives from the clubhead of a driver.

It has been proved by laboratory tests at the Bureau of Standards in America that a ball loses some of its liveliness when hit hard. To get some idea of the amount of this loss, suppose a perfectly elastic ball is reckoned as 100%. The modern ball is then 81% elastic for gentle blows but only 71 % elastic if hit hard.

You may ask how much extra distance would one obtain if the modern ball had the same elasticity when hit hard as it has when dropped from 10 ft (say) on to a concrete floor, i.e. if its elasticity remained at 81% of perfect elasticity instead of dropping to 71% under playing conditions. You might think that the distance would go up in proportion to the elasticity, i.e. in the ratio 81 to 71, in which case a 200 yard drive would become 227 yd. and a 260 yd. drive 295 yd. But you would be wrong, for the true increase would be in the ratio 1.81 to 1.71 - a very much less significant increase. It raises the 200 yd. drive to 212 yd. and the 260 yd. drive to 275 yd. - increases of only 6% compared with 14% if distance was directly proportional to elasticity.

Now it is pretty certain that the modern ball, with its 71% elasticity when hit hard, can never be developed to give an elasticity figure higher than 81%, which it now possesses only for light blows. This is equivalent to saying that 6% is the maximum gain in distance which any manufacturer, British or American, can achieve by making the ball more elastic - or more lively if you prefer that word. It is worth noting indeed that the gain would only be 17% if the ball was 100% elastic - something that can never be approached for golf balls.

What sets a limit to increases in ball elasticity and what no ingenuity on the part of the ball manufacturer can overcome is the fact that the ball they are in quest of *must in addition not be appreciably harder* or less resilient than the present ball. That indeed is where the rub comes. To manufacture a ball that is more elastic than the 81% figure above suggested as a limit is not in itself so difficult if resilience or degree of softness did not count. When, however, the ball has to be flexible enough, as the modern ball certainly is, to flatten itself into a hemisphere against the face of the clubhead and still be more than 71% elastic, the problem becomes insuperable.

A hollow glass or steel ball, while more elastic than any golf ball, would be impossible to play with even if the weight was right. Hit with a wooden club, it would not be the ball that would deform but the clubhead, and that to the point of disintegration. Cotton's[*] verdict after trying a very hard super-elastic golf ball was that it felt like hitting a stone.

What it amounts to is that, at impact, the more elastic but harder ball suffers·a greater force over a shorter time than the standard ball. The result is that very fast vibrations - faster even than the 30 per sec. vibration of Fig. 11(b) - are set up, and these are the prime causes of the stinging sensation in the hands, which for example accompanies an iron shot hit 'thin'.

One's final conclusion is that the present golf ball cannot be greatly improved upon. A gain of about 6% in distance is the very maximum that ball manufacturers can hope to achieve if given a free hand. There seems therefore little point in trying to impose an artificial limit on ball elasticity with all its attendant complications. The efforts of the U.S.G.A. in this direction seem therefore to be singularly ill advised.

---

[*]   'Golfing Album' - Country Life, 1959.

CHAPTER XIV

A RATIONAL APPROACH TO THE PUTTING PROBLEM

There is probably more nonsense talked and written about putting than about any other aspect of the game of golf. Each writer on the subject has his own pet theories, and these are usually expounded at inordinate length. Long putts, medium putts and short putts, uphill putts and downhill putts, putts on fast greens and putts on slow greens are all treated in such portentous detail as to leave the reader in a proper 'tizzy'. The psychological side of the problem is given no less prominence than the technical side. Why are short putts of three or four feet missed by top-class players? Is it due to the lack of sufficient care or is it due to taking too much care? Or is it due to failure either in lining up the putt or in maintaining that line during the putting stroke? These are the kind of questions that are discussed ad lib. in the putting section of instructional books.

The trouble is that nothing very constructive ever seems to emerge from these long-drawn-out discussions and the reader is left very little wiser than before. One well known American golfer for example, after devoting many pages to the inner mysteries of the putting stroke and their dependence on the physical and mental attitude of the player, has in the end nothing more informative to impart than to advocate keeping the putter head square to the line of flight as it approaches the ball and keeping it still square in the follow-through. His readers may justifiably retort, 'Yes, yes, we know all about that, but just tell us how it is to be accomplished.'

I like Dai Rees's frankness when, after advocating 'a relaxed mind, confidence and then a smooth, unhurried stroke' he hands the hypothetical reader, who complains that he can neither relax nor muster up confidence, the somewhat brutal answer 'Then, my friend, I am sorry for you!'

What I propose to do here is to approach the putting problem in the way that I should approach a scientific problem. First, to obtain a clear appreciation of the difficulties that have to be overcome and second, to devise a method of overcoming them.

Let me make it clear that I am not here concerned with the problem of judging the effects of sloping greens and the quality and lie of the grass. These factors need to be taken into account of course but they are not amenable to a scientific discussion. What I am concerned with is the problem of lining up the clubface in the required direction and in moving the clubhead along the chosen line while keeping the face square to it; also of course the problem of the strength of the stroke.

Even when these problems are solved, putting across a sloping green can still result in failure because of the added difficulty that the strength of the shot is no longer independent of its aim as it is on a level surface. A six-foot putt on a level surface requires only squaring up the putter blade with the hole and keeping it that way; the danger of badly overshooting is negligible and therefore there is no real problem in judging the strength of the putt. By contrast, the same six-footer across a sloping green is a lot more difficult, for the line is no longer in the direction of the hole but has to be judged in relation to the speed of the ball and therefore of the strength of the shot.

Granting all this, the fact remains that solving the twin problems of correctly lining up the putter-blade and keeping it square to that line during the stroke would undoubtedly drastically reduce the number of missed six-footers, and make the missing of three or four-footers exceptional. This is conclusively proved by the experiments that Dr. Cochran and his colleagues described in their recently published book*. There they compare the performance of a 'perfect' machine with that of professional golfers. From six feet on a good green the machine missed only 2% of putts whereas the pro's missed 45%. If they could sink say 75% of the six-footers instead of only 55%, it must follow that the score for a complete round would be significantly improved.

The problem of lining up a putt

Of the twin problems of lining up the putter blade and keeping it on the chosen line during the stroke, the first is without question the easier of the two. I am referring now to straightforward putt on a fairly level green. Although the easier of the two problems it is nevertheless of paramount importance. For remember that an error of only 1^0 in aligning the blade represents an error of 1.25 inches at the hole in a putt of 6 ft - quite enough to spell failure unless the ball has lost all speed as it reaches the hole.

Now what is the most effective way of lining up the blade so as to be as nearly at right angles with the line to the hole as possible? It is certainly not by standing over the ball in the customary putting stance and looking sideways along that line. The fact that this entails turning the head, as the ball and the hole are alternately brought into focus, is alone enough to damn such a method. Yet it is the method that is almost universally used.

One would think that it is pretty obvious that for effectively lining up the blade two fundamental conditions need to be satisfied.

(i) That the forward top edge of the blade be straight and sharp and dead parallel with the front and back edges of the base which should also be sharp and parallel with each other.

(ii) That the process of lining up be done without moving the head but by a slight movement of the eyes alone.

---

* *loc. cit. p. 107.*

Condition (i) has to do with the design of the head and a few words on that subject need to be said.

A suitable design of head is roughly indicated in Fig. 17(a) and (b). Fig. 17(a) is a view of the clubhead looking down on it from the front. Most of the weight is concentrated at the two ends of the blade with the line of the shaft passing close to the centre of gravity of the head. The aligning edge is the top forward edge AB which is parallel to the horizontal base edges CD and EF of the two ends and the slightly recessed base LM.

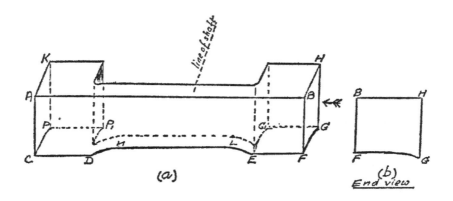

Fig. 17. Outline of suggested putter head

Note also that the base edge FG (like the corresponding edge at the other end) is 'hollow ground' i.e. concave looked at from below, as is more clearly shown in the end view (b). The reason for these design features will emerge in the course of the next few paragraphs.

I have suggested a blade slightly longer than the conventional length because that makes it easier to place it at right angles to the desired line.

The 'modus operandi' is now as follows. You are in the address position with the ball opposite the middle of the face which points roughly in the direction of the hole. Incidentally the putter will have a shaft some 10° to the vertical at address, so as to comply with the latest regulation governing the angle between the blade and the shaft. Now step back about a yard and place yourself so that, looking forward, you see the ball and the hole in your direct line of vision. In stepping back you keep your left hand in contact with the butt of the shaft by rocking the blade on to the rear edges and of the two ends, which then alone make contact with the ground. In this way the forward top edge AB comes clearly into view and your job now is to adjust the position of the clubhead so as to set it at right angles to the line connecting the ball to the hole. By virtue of standing well back from the ball and the adjacent blade you can make this adjustment by merely running your eye up and down the line with no movement of the head. If you had a sufficiently long T square you could test your lining up ability directly by using the edge AB as a base for it.

I have pretty good proof that it is possible to line up a blade with considerable accuracy as the following experience shows. Some time ago, before the croquet mallet type of putter was banned, I conceived the notion of using that type of putter with a cylindrical head in a novel way. The idea was to hold it so that the shaft slopes forward at about 30° to the horizontal. The player faces the hole and holds the club with the right hand close to the right hip and left hand some 18 inches further down the 4 ft. long shaft - in much the same way as one would hold a garden rake. Aim is taken by bringing the shaft into line with the ball and the hole, and the shot is made by sliding the head along the ground to meet the ball in a crisp impact. The fact of the head being at right angles to the shaft necessarily sets it at right angles also with the line of the hole once the shaft lies on that line. I found this method quite deadly and completely jitter-proof, because, once the head was lined it remained lined up by virtue of its contact with the ground which prevented any twist of the shaft. From 6 feet I could sink putts almost as well as the machine already referred to - at any rate a good 90% which puts the 55% professional performance in the shade. Even before the banning of the mallet type putter the R. & A. Club declared against the method. There was no objection to the putter as such, as it was then legal, but only to the method of making the stroke. It was judged to be a push and not a proper stroke. I was never able to understand that verdict because it seemed to me that the stroke was no more a push than the quite legal stroke in which the shaft is moved parallel to itself rather than swung.

However, the point is that the reason why the method was so deadly was the fact that it ensured the set of the head being maintained during the stroke. But that would be useless unless the original line-up were correct. The conclusion therefore is that, by standing well behind the ball while facing the hole, it is possible to set the face of the putter with great accuracy.

The situation now reached is that the clubhead, with the edge AB square to the hole, is resting on the turf, contact with which is made only on the sharp rear edges PP_1 and GG_1 of the end blocks. The shaft, with the fingertips of the left hand still in contact with the butt end, is now moved back into the customary address position by rocking the head about the sharp edges just mentioned. You will now understand why the head is designed to avoid contact with the ground except along the rear edges of the base. It ensures that the original square setting of the top edge AB of the blade, and hence of its striking face, is meticulously preserved. Note that the leading edge F of the base in view (b) is a shade higher than the rear edge G in order that, even in the address position the blade still rests solidly on the rear setting edges.

The great advantage of this pre-setting is that, in making the stroke, you *no longer have to bother about direction but only about strength*. There is therefore no need for interminably turning the head from ball to hole and back again, which is the result of trying to gauge strength and direction at the same time. A glance or two is enough to gauge the distance, after which there is only one thing left - to keep the face square while executing the stroke. That is now the crux of the problem. To succeed, it is necessary to move the club as little as possible, which means making the stroke as short as possible - not more than about 3 inches for a 6 ft. putt.

Before describing the procedure for making such a putt I would like to say a word on the question of muscular control - how muscular control is affected by the importance of the occasion. When a player is confronted with the situation where he has 'this putt for the open', it is useless for him to try to banish the importance of the occasion from his mind. It cannot be done. He must concentrate on the job in hand despite the crushing awareness of the dire consequence of failure. Nothing but strong nerves will suffice and that means that 'anno domini' has not yet gained the upper hand. Hundreds of nervous examples spring to mind of the crippling effects of tension. Have you ever tried scaling a 60 ft ladder? Up to 20 or 30 ft. you climb in a relaxed fashion, but the higher you climb beyond that the more conscious you become of the danger of a false step or a careless hand grip. A conflict arises between the conscious and the sub-conscious mind. Despite the subconscious mind's assurance that it is quite capable of dealing with the situation, and indeed despite the fact that the conscious mind knows this to be true, the conscious mind will insist on interfering, with the result that the grip of the hands on the rungs of the ladder becomes tighter and tighter and so muscularly exhausting as to precipitate the very danger they try to avert.

Walking a hundred yards along a two-foot plank is childs play, but if that plank bridges a chasm a hundred feet deep the task takes on a different complexion.

In neither of these examples is nicety of control demanded. When it is, the task becomes even more formidable. Even such a simple action as signing one's name to an important document cannot be done with quite the same easy abandon as when, for example, signing a cheque. In signing the cheque you use the flexibility of the fingers, but the more important signature tends to freeze the delicate control of the fingers and the whole hand comes into the affair, and any attempt to maintain finger flexibility by effort of will merely leads to a highly unusual signature.

This illustrates the well known physiological fact that it is the more sensitive and delicate muscles that are the most difficult to control under nervous tension. This is the reason why it is on the putting green that once great players first begin to lose their touch. While their shots through the green may still be second to none, their reserve of nervous energy is unequal to the demands made on it when crucial putts are in question.

Now my thesis here is that, since it is the more powerful muscles of the body that are the least susceptible to nervous tension, why not use them exclusively in the putting stroke. In other words, why not putt with the hips and so cut out the less dependable wrists, arms and shoulders. For this purpose the club and the upper parts of the body are to be visualised as an integral block, to be moved only by the hips. The elbows are stuck firmly into the body and at the same time pressed together the better to identify them with the hip movement. The hands grip the clubshaft, not merely firmly but rather with the proverbial vice-like grip, thus completely restricting its movement to that prescribed by the hips.

Note how such a powerful grip makes a virtue of necessity. It cashes in on the natural tendency to tense up and grip the club hard under nervous tension. Not for our purpose to take Bobby Locke's advice for crucial putts, 'The more important the putt the gentler the grip', for such advice pre-supposes an ability to control the gentler grip.

The situation now is that the putter head is resting horizontally on the ground, contact with which is made by the sharp rear edges of the base of the blade. There is therefore little danger of its angle of set being disturbed as the shaft is brought into the address position. You now take up your stance without any reference to the hole but only by reference to the set of the face. In other words, with feet well apart and knees bent, you choose your stance in the way that will allow you most easily to move the clubhead perpendicularly to the face; you concentrate on placing your feet so as to make the natural direction of your stroke coincide with the perpendicular to the face. Note again; no reference any more to the hole but only to the club face.

One most important point must be mentioned. It concerns weight distribution and the position of the feet relative to the ball at address. *The weight should be almost entirely on the left foot with the ball slightly forward of the left heel*, thus bringing the putter head opposite the left heel at address. The right foot should be some 15 inches from the left foot and on a line parallel to the line of the putt.

You are now set for the putt, with the clubhead just behind the ball. One good look at the hole *for distance only* should be enough. For 6 foot putts and the like a 2 or 3 inch back stroke is ample - slow back and a sharp forward stroke of the required strength. The onus of maintaining the set of the face is on the hips, and the chances of success in this, as in every other department of the game, are necessarily improved by practice.

You might think that control of the strength of a putt must be less reliable when made by the above method than when it is made by a smooth flowing stroke with plenty of wrist movement. You would be wrong. You can easily prove this by straightforward trial; place a mark on your carpet and check how close to it you can play your ball from various distances, using first the conventional method and then the method above described, making some allowance for the fact that the technique must feel a little strange at first.

What is delightful about the technique is the way it cuts out the need for that interminable turning of the head between ball and hole, which is such a noticeable feature of the present day method. With the new method one look at the hole for the purpose of gauging the strength of the putt is adequate, after which the mind is focussed on maintaining the existing correct face setting during the very short stroke, which is all that the powerful yet sensitive muscles of the legs and hips need to propel the ball the required distance.

A major advantage of the technique is that, while naturally requiring a modicum of practice, its efficiency does not demand the incessant practice which is the price of maintaining a high standard of putting by the conventional method. In all physical activities, the best technique requires the least practice.

That the conventional method of putting makes use of an unsound technique seems to me to be proved by the statistical fact already mentioned - that top-class professionals can do no better than sink about half of their six-foot putts. And this raises the question of what precisely it is that makes it an unsound method.

To answer that question let us first be quite clear what is meant by the conventional method. From watching top-class professionals and from reading their books it becomes pretty clear that the overwhelming majority of them putt with the wrists - almost entirely with the wrists for short putts and with wrists and arms for longer putts. A minority rely on making the putting stroke with arms and wrists moving as one rigid unit with no shoulder movement. Still another and smaller minority use a shoulder-rocking movement in which the arms and hands move rigidly with the shoulders. It is obvious that these minorities are agreed on one point - that wrists are not to be trusted under tension.

The great majority of players, however, both flex their wrists and move their arms in the putting stroke and this must therefore be regarded as the conventional method. Its advocates may be further sub-divided into those who tap their short putts and swing their longer putts and yet those others who insist on using a smooth swinging action for all putts - the latter again in the majority. They all, however, with rare exceptions strive to keep the blade moving on the chosen line with the face at right angles to that line throughout the stroke - on the back stroke, the forward stroke and the follow-through.

It is a very difficult task which they attempt, for, simple though it appears, the wrist action it involves is a most complicated one. It is little wonder therefore that only incessant practice can ensure a modicum of success; for 45% failure on a six-foot putt cannot by any standard be regarded as more than a modicum. What is astonishing though is that, fully conscious as they must be of the vital importance of keeping the face of the blade square to the hole, they still take the most incredible liberties with that objective. One familiar ritual followed by some players is to ground the blade in front of the ball -presumably to obtain an unimpeded view of the line to the hole - then, after setting the face to their satisfaction, they lift it in order to ground it behind the ball before finally making their stroke. One might well comment 'How irrational can you get?' For surely, the accuracy lost due to setting the face with the blade grounded behind the ball rather than in front is a good deal less than the accuracy lost through lifting the blade from front to back. One degree out is enough to spoil a six foot putt, and to lift a grounded clubhead from front to back of the ball without changing its angle by a single degree requires either exceptional control or exceptional luck.

Traditional methods and ideas have, however, a surprising vitality. One of these is the notion that the putter face should strike the ball on an upward arc so as to give it top spin. Such an idea could never have been conceived by anyone with the most elementary acquaintance with mechanics. Top spin is only to be generated if the line of the contact force passes above the centre of gravity of the ball, and it is impossible with a zero-loft putter to get enough angle of rise to achieve this to any useful degree. It is certainly out of the question if Gary Player's advice[*] to 'hit the centre of the ball with the centre of the clubface' is followed. It is also clearly out of the question for putters with a slight loft. Yet Jim Ferrier[**], in his discussion on putting, lays great emphasis on the importance of the putter blade being on an upward arc after striking the ball, because in his words 'the ball is thus given a maximum of overspin' in order to 'obtain a smooth roll'.

That such ideas have no foundation in fact has now been further demonstrated by scientifically controlled experiments[***], which show conclusively that the way it is struck has *no influence on the way the ball rolls*. It appears that, in whatever way it is struck the ball invariably skids over something like the first 20% of its total travel before it starts rolling properly.

All this goes to support the view that no golfer need hesitate to try out revolutionary techniques just because they run counter to traditional ideas.

---

[*]   'Positive Golf' (Cassell 1967)

[**]   'The Golf Clinic' (Nicholas Kaye, 1950)

[***] 'The Search for the perfect swing' by A. Cochran and J. Stobbs (Heinemann, 1968)

APPENDIX

Quarterly Journal of
Mechanics and Applied
Mathematics

VOLUME XX   PART 2

MAY 1967

THE DYNAMICS OF THE GOLF SWING

(with Conclusions of Practical Interest)

By D. WILLIAMS (*Farnborough*)

[Received 8 March 1966. Revise 3 October 1966]

SUMMARY

The way in which a first-class player applies power during a golf swing is deduced from a few basic data obtained from a well-known (Spalding) multi-flash photograph of Bobby Jones swinging a driver. Conclusions of practical interest are drawn which throw light on certain aspects of the golf swing that have been the subject of considerable argument over the years.

1. Introduction

To investigate the dynamics of the golf swing is to tackle a problem that is rather different from the run of dynamical problems. What is usually required in such problems is to determine the motion of a system under applied forces that are specified. In the golf swing, on the contrary, it is the motion of the club as photographically observed, that is specified and the problem is to find what forces must have been applied to it to produce that motion. Innumerable cinematograph pictures of the swings of leading players have been taken in the past. Some of these have been sophisticated enough to show the practically instantaneous position of the club at short and regular time intervals throughout the swing. No one questions the accuracy of such photographic records, and there is general agreement on what position the club takes up relative to the position of the player's body at all stages of the swing. Where there is disagreement, and indeed strong disagreement, is in the interpretation of such cine-photographs. This disagreement is natural enough, because the pictures do not show what forces the player applies to the club. Nor does the player himself understand where and how he converts the physical power of his body into kinetic energy of the clubhead. Some of the most distinguished exponents of the game have been wide of the mark when they have tried to interpret their own action photographs, as their published views amply demonstrate. The result of such misinterpretation is often to attach undue importance to certain muscular actions that can be shown to be in fact of only minor significance.

In view of what has just been said above, it may be accepted that an attempt at explaining what really happens during a golf swing should not be without practical interest.

[Quart. Journ. Mech. and Applied Math., Vol. XX, Pt. 2, 1967]

2. General approach to the problem

The method adopted in the present approach is to take as a basis a well-known multi-flash photograph† of Bobby Jones swinging a driver (Fig. 1). In this the position of club and player is recorded throughout the downswing at intervals of 1/100 second. The teed-up ball, which appears in each flash photograph, offers a convenient standard against which to measure the relevant distances and hence to

FIG. 1

estimate the velocities of hands and clubhead at all stages of the swing. The more or less standard length of the clubshaft offers another useful yardstick for this purpose. Data collected in this way (with due account taken of the angle between the plane of the swing and the ground), while not exact, is accurate enough for all practical purposes. As the exposure time for each flash is only 1/100,000 of a second each photograph stands out clearly and there is no distortion.

From an examination of this picture and of a great many continuous-action cine-photographs (1) of other first-class players, one basic fact stands out. This is that the downswing in golf up to the moment of impact divides itself naturally into two distinct stages. In the first

† Supplied to me by courtesy of A. G. Spalding Bros. Incorp., Chipokee, Mass., U.S.A.

stage, shoulders, arms, hands and clubshaft move together as a rigid body about a fixed axis of rotation (making an angle of about 40° to the horizontal) and therefore with a common angular acceleration. It follows that the angle between arm and clubshaft—the so called *wrist-cock*—remains unchanged during this stage.

In the second stage of the downswing the wrist-cock angle opens out, slowly at first but more rapidly as it nears the point of impact, where of course arm and clubshaft come into line in the same vertical plane and the wrist-cock disappears. From examining the Jones picture one concludes that the angular velocity of the hands about the axis of rotation is substantially constant during the second stage. This may not be strictly true but is near enough to the truth to justify the assumption of constant hand velocity over the second stage of the swing.

The hands are assumed to travel in a circle about the (fixed) axis of rotation. This is nearly enough true and simplifies the analysis. In brief, therefore, what we are assuming is that the hands during the first stage gain a velocity that during the second stage remains constant. It is further assumed that the clubhead remains always in the plane of the circle traced by the hands. In practice neither the hands nor the clubhead move precisely in the same common plane but corrections due to any movement out of that plane can safely be neglected.

One of the first points to settle is where, in the (approximately) circular travel of the hands, the first stage ends and the second stage begins. By careful examination of the multi-flash Jones picture and of action photographs of other famous players it would seem that the transition occurs after an angular movement of between 60° and 70°. The precise value is not of great importance and must vary somewhat from player to player. What has just been said applies to the full-blooded shot with a driver; for iron clubs the transition occurs earlier.

Other assumptions and observed data are as follows:

(i) The radius of the circle traced by the hands is taken to be 2·2 ft. This is a good enough approximation to what must vary from player to player.

(ii) Knowing the clubhead velocity at impact (i.e. 165 ft/sec) it is possible to deduce the constant angular velocity ω_0 during the second stage.

(iii) The angular velocity ω_0 obtained in (ii) fixes the terminal velocity of the first stage and the question arises as to what kind of acceleration produces that terminal velocity. An invaluable guide to this acceleration is the known fact that the moment applied by the hands, i.e. the resultant transverse inertia force at the clubhead multiplied by the length of the shaft, cannot much exceed 3 lb ft which corresponds to a transverse inertia force of about 1 lb. Any force greater than this would produce a degree of bending of the shaft greater than that shown in the photograph. The value chosen for the wrist moment in the analysis is determined by the further consideration that the time covered by the first stage must agree with the observed time as recorded on the photograph. By limiting the wrist moment in this way and assuming the terminal velocity known, it is possible to derive the motion of the club throughout the first stage.

(iv) The transition from the first to the second stage of the downswing raises a problem, because the assumed sudden drop in acceleration must in actual fact be a gradual drop. This is a point discussed later in the analysis.

(v) For the purpose of the analysis the inertia of the club is represented by that of two masses, the first is situated at the hands and the second at a distance from the hands equal to the length of the equivalent simple pendulum. This equivalent shaft length is given as a in Fig. 2 and the equivalent second mass is taken to be m. For the driver used by Jones, typical values are 2·75 ft for a and 0·0214 slug ($=$ 11 oz) for m.

3. Mathematical analysis

3.1. *First stage of downswing*

In Fig. 2 the plane xy represents the plane of the swing in which the hands and clubhead move. The fixed axis of rotation normal to the

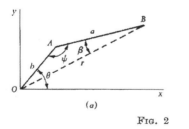
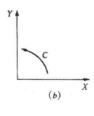

(a)   (b)

FIG. 2

plane xy cuts it at O. The hands, represented by the point A, move in a circular path about the fixed centre O and the clubhead B describes a circle relative to the hands as centre. The radius OA will be referred to as the arm (although not a physical arm). A and B are mutual centres of percussion for the club and AB will be referred to as the 'equivalent shaft' or 'the shaft' when there is no ambiguity. Let $OA = b$. $AB = a$, $OB = r$, the angle $OAB = \psi$ and the angle $AOx = \theta$.

In the first stage of the motion ψ remains constant at ψ_0 so that the arm OA and shaft AB rotate together as a rigid body, the hands at A and the clubhead at B tracing out circular paths of fixed radii b and r_0 respectively. Relative to coordinate axes Ox, Oy, the position of the club head for any value of ψ is given by

$$x = b \cos \theta + a \cos(\theta + \psi - \pi), \tag{1}$$

$$y = b \sin \theta + a \sin(\theta + \psi - \pi). \tag{2}$$

The forces and moment applied by the hands in the sense indicated in Fig. 2(b) are therefore given as follows:

$$\frac{X}{m} = \ddot{x} = -b\dot{\theta}^2 \cos \theta - b\ddot{\theta} \sin \theta - a\dot{\theta}^2 \cos(\theta + \psi_0 - \pi) - a\ddot{\theta} \sin(\theta + \psi_0 - \pi), \tag{3}$$

$$\frac{Y}{m} = \ddot{y} = -b\dot{\theta}^2 \sin \theta + b\ddot{\theta} \cos \theta - a\dot{\theta}^2 \sin(\theta + \psi_0 - \pi) + a\ddot{\theta} \cos(\theta + \psi_0 - \pi), \tag{4}$$

$$\frac{C}{m} = -ab\dot{\theta}^2 \sin \psi_0 - ab\ddot{\theta} \cos \psi_0 + a^2\ddot{\theta}, \tag{5}$$

where use has been made of the geometrical equations

$$b \sin \psi = r \sin \beta, \qquad (a - b \cos \psi) = r \cos \beta. \tag{6}$$

If P is the constant transverse shear force in the shaft due to the wrist moment C,

$$C = Pa \tag{7}$$

and, as already noted, the force P cannot be greater than a pound or two. If, further, P is assumed to be constant at P_0 during the first stage, its numerical value can be determined from the fact that the angle θ_f at the transition point between the two stages (i.e. at the point where ψ is judged from the photograph to begin to open) can be fairly closely estimated). As will be shown later the value of the constant angular velocity ω_0 of the arm OA during the second stage can be calculated from the known clubhead speed at impact. With θ_f and ω_0 known, the value of the constant P_0 must be so chosen as to make the time taken for θ to increase in magnitude to θ_f equal to that recorded in the photograph. On this basis the value of P_0 works out later at 1 lb.

In the work that follows we needs must assign representative numerical values to the physical and geometrical quantities involved, because it is only by comparing numerical results derived via the analysis with those measured from the photograph that it is possible to establish the authenticity of the analytical approach. We therefore take

whence

$$
\left.\begin{aligned}
P_0 &= 1\,\text{lb (so far tentative)}, \\
OA &= b = 2{\cdot}2\ \text{ft}, \\
AB &= a = 2{\cdot}75\ \text{ft}, \\
\angle BAO &= \psi_0 = 65^\circ, \\
OB &= r = 2{\cdot}7\ \text{ft}, \\
\angle ABO &= \beta = 48^\circ, \\
m &= 11\ \text{oz} = 0{\cdot}0214\ \text{slug}.
\end{aligned}\right\}
\tag{8}
$$

Putting $P_0 a$ for C in (5), we have (since $r_0 = a - b\cos\psi_0$)

$$
\ddot{\theta} - \left(\frac{b\sin\psi_0}{a - b\cos\psi_0}\right)\dot{\theta}^2 = \frac{P_0/m}{(a - b\cos\psi_0)}.
\tag{9}
$$

On integration and putting $\theta = 0$ at zero time, we obtain

$$
\dot{\theta}^2 = \frac{P_0}{mb\sin\psi_0}\{\exp(2\theta\tan\beta) - 1\}
\tag{10}
$$

and

$$
\ddot{\theta} = \frac{P_0/m}{a - b\cos\psi_0}\exp(2\theta\tan\beta).
\tag{11}
$$

At the end of the first stage,

$$
\dot{\theta} = \dot{\theta}_f = \omega_0
$$

so that, from (10),

$$
\omega^2 = \frac{P_0}{b\sin\psi_0}\{\exp(2\theta_f\tan\beta) - 1\}.
\tag{10a}
$$

To derive the numerical value of ω_0 it is necessary to consider the second stage of the downswing.

3.2. *Second stage of downswing*

During the second stage of the downswing the angle ψ between arm and shaft progressively increases from ψ_0 to the value π at impact, when the shaft AB comes into line with the arm OA.

It is clear from the photograph that the moment Pa exerted by the wrists during the second stage drops from $P_0 a$ to a negligible value just before impact. For the pronounced bend in the shaft, noticeable in the tenth exposure (counting back from the ball), has disappeared by the time the fifth exposure takes place, when the shaft is again straight. The slight forward bend that takes place in the last few exposures before impact is fully accounted for by the fact that the heavy inertia pull of the head acts along the line connecting the centre of gravity of the head to the hands, thus causing a bending action that bows the shaft towards that line. A suitable expression for P is therefore

$$P = P_0 \exp\{-(\psi-\psi_0)\}, \tag{12}$$

which is very small when ψ reaches the value π. The legitimacy of making P drop in this way can only be established by comparing the displacements of hands and clubhead derived on that basis with those recorded in the photograph at each exposure.

Equations (3), (4) and (5) now become (since θ has the constant value ω_0 and therefore $\ddot\theta$ is zero)

$$\left.\begin{aligned}\frac{X}{m} &= \ddot x = -b\dot\theta^2\cos\theta - a(\dot\theta+\dot\psi)^2\cos(\theta+\psi-\pi) - a\ddot\psi\sin(\theta+\psi-\pi),\\ \frac{Y}{m} &= \ddot y = -b\dot\theta^2\sin\theta - a(\dot\theta+\dot\psi)^2\sin(\theta+\psi-\pi) + a\ddot\psi\cos(\theta+\psi-\pi),\end{aligned}\right\} \tag{13}$$

$$\frac{P}{m} = -b\dot\theta^2\sin\psi + a\ddot\psi. \tag{14}$$

Using (12), we have from (14)

$$\ddot\psi = (b/a)\dot\theta^2\sin\psi + (P_0/ma)\exp\{-(\psi-\psi_0)\}.$$

On integration and taking initial conditions $\psi=\psi_0$, $\dot\psi=\dot\psi_0$, we obtain

$$\dot\psi^2 = 2(b/a)\omega_0^2(\cos\psi_0-\cos\psi)+(2P_0/ma)[1-\exp\{-(\psi-\psi_0)\}]+\dot\psi_0^2, \tag{15}$$

and therefore

$$(\dot\psi^2)_{\psi=\pi} = 2(b/a)\omega_0^2(\cos\psi_0+1)+(2P_0/ma)[1-\exp\{-(\pi-\psi_0)\}]+\dot\psi_0^2. \tag{15a}$$

Since we know the clubhead velocity at impact (measured from the Jones photo record) we have another relation between $\dot\psi$ and ω_0 at impact. This gives the velocity v of the actual clubhead, distant $1\cdot2a$ from the hands, as

$$v = (1\cdot2a+b)\omega_0 + 1\cdot2a\dot\psi_{(\psi=\pi)}, \tag{16}$$

so that

$$(\dot\psi^2)_{\psi=\pi} = \left\{\frac{v-(1\cdot2a+b)\omega_0}{1\cdot2a}\right\}^2. \tag{17}$$

It is convenient here to put in the numerical values of the various quantities. We take those given in (8) above.

From (15a), then,

$$\dot\psi^2 = 2\cdot27\omega_0^2 + 29\cdot5 + \dot\psi_0^2 \tag{18}$$

and from (17)

$$\dot\psi^2 = 2500 - 167\omega_0 + 2\cdot8\omega_0^2. \tag{19}$$

Equating (18) and (19), we have

$$\omega_0^2 - 315\omega_0 + (4680 - 1{\cdot}89\dot{\psi}_0^2) = 0. \tag{20}$$

As will be shown later $1{\cdot}89\dot{\psi}_0^2$ is small enough to be neglected compared with 4680, so that the roots of the quadratic (20) become $\omega_0 = 157{\cdot}5 \pm 142$ and therefore

$$\omega_0 = 15{\cdot}5 \text{ rad/sec.} \tag{21}$$

Using this value of ω_0 in equation (10a), we have

$$(15{\cdot}5)^2 = \frac{1}{0{\cdot}0214 \times 2{\cdot}2 \times \sin 65^\circ}\{\exp(2{\cdot}22\theta_f) - 1\} = 23{\cdot}5\{\exp(2{\cdot}22\theta_f) - 1\} \tag{22}$$

which gives

$$\theta_f = 1{\cdot}09 \text{ rad}(= 62{\cdot}5^\circ). \tag{23}$$

This value of θ_f agrees well enough with what can be observed from the Jones picture, i.e. that the transition between the rigid-body rotation characterising the first stage of the motion and the second stage of constant hand velocity occurs at a value of θ_f of between 60° and 70°. *The tentative value of 1 lb assumed above for the force P_0 is therefore justified.*

There is a further check that can be applied to the value of θ_f as derived above, in that the time taken for θ to increase from zero to θ_f must agree with what can be directly observed in the Jones picture. This check will be applied later in this paper. For the moment we need to settle the question of the value of $\dot{\psi}_0$. To do this we apply the condition that the moment of the force applied by the player about the centre of rotation O must be continuous at the transition between the two stages of the motion. This makes

$$\dot{\psi}_0 = 5{\cdot}6 \text{ rad/sec.} \tag{24}$$

In satisfying conditions of continuity of angular velocity $\dot{\theta}$ and of applied moment at the instant of change from the first to the second stage of the motion, we have necessarily introduced a discontinuity in $\dot{\psi}$. Immediately before the change, $\dot{\psi}$ is zero, but immediately after the change it needs to have the value 5·6 rad/sec, as given by (24) if the moment of the force applied by the player is to be continuous. The actual process of transition between the first and second stages is not a sudden change of $\ddot{\theta}$ from $\ddot{\theta}_f$ to zero, as we have assumed, nor is the change in $\dot{\psi}_0$ a sudden change from zero to $\dot{\psi}_0$. In point of fact the angular velocity $\dot{\theta}_f$ ($= \omega_1$ say) at the end of the first stage is something less than the steady value ω_0 that has been assumed above for the whole of the second stage. What happens is that during the initial part of the second stage the applied moment is partly equilibrated by the moment $mr_0^2\ddot{\theta}$, which gradually diminishes to zero as $\dot{\theta}$ increases from ω_1 to ω_0, and partly by the growing moment of the other inertia forces.

The precise relation between these moments during the comparatively short transition period cannot readily be derived analytically, nor is it important to an understanding of the salient characteristics of the golf swing.

The effect of the discontinuity is shown clearly in the curve of velocity of Fig. 6 as the step AB. The true shape is along some such curve as EF which is shown dotted in the figure.

4. Results

Displacement θ as a function of time during first stage of motion

The time to reach any value θ in the first stage is given by

$$t = \int_0^\theta \frac{d\theta}{\dot{\theta}}. \tag{25}$$

Using (10), and carrying out the integration, we find that it takes 0·24 sec for θ to reach θ_f as given by (23). This is in satisfactory agreement with the Jones multi-flash picture, which appears to show that the wrists are beginning to uncock after about 24 inter-flash intervals of 0·01 sec each. Part AB of the curve of Fig. 3 shows θ plotted on a time base. Until we know the time taken for ψ to increase from ψ_0 to π the straight line part of the curve for the second stage cannot be drawn.

Displacement ψ as a function of time during second stage of downswing

To reach any value of ψ from ψ_0 requires a time

$$t = \int_{\psi_0}^\psi \frac{d\psi}{\dot{\psi}}. \tag{26}$$

Using equation (15) for $\dot{\psi}$ and integrating, we obtain t in terms of ψ and therefore can plot ψ on a time base. This is done in Fig. 4, which shows that the total time for the second stage is 0·116 sec—time for 12 exposures at 0·01 sec intervals. Counting back 12 exposures from the impact position in the Jones picture we see that the player's wrists are then just about beginning to uncock. Agreement is therefore very satisfactory.

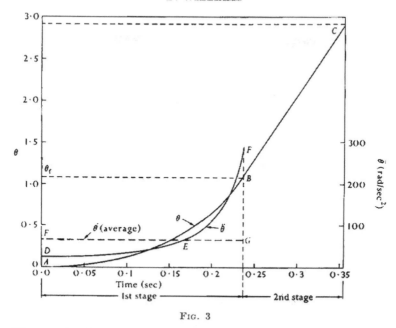

Fig. 3

The angular displacement θ of the hands at any time t from the start of the second stage is equal to $\omega_0 t$ where ω_0 has the constant value 15·5 reached at the end of the first stage. The part BC of the curve shown in Fig. 3 is therefore a straight line with a slope equal to the slope at B of the curve AB. The total angular movement of the hands for the second stage is thus

$$\theta_2 = 15{\cdot}5 \times 0{\cdot}116 = 1{\cdot}8 \text{ rad}(= 103°), \tag{27}$$

which is in good agreement with the photograph.

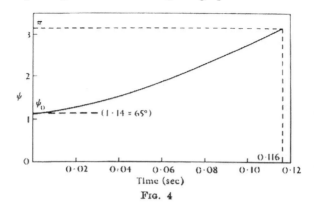

Fig. 4

Successive positions of hands and clubshaft for the complete downswing

By making use of Figs. 3 and 4, it is now possible to show the successive relative positions of the hands and the clubshaft throughout the downswing at the same time intervals (0·01 sec) as the successive flash photographs of the Jones picture. This is done in Fig. 5.

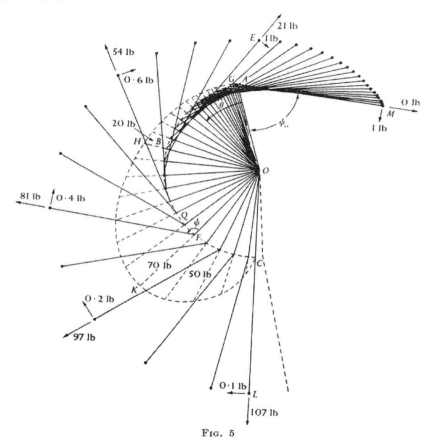

Fig. 5

The rigid body rotation, which constitutes the first stage of the downswing, is indicated by the arc *AB* for the hands and *ME* for the clubhead. During the second stage the hands move from *B* to *C* over the arc *BC* at the constant angular velocity ω_0, so that equal arcs are traversed in equal times. With ω_0 having the value 15·5 rad/sec, an arc of 0·155 rad. (= 8·9°) is traversed in each 0·01 sec and the corresponding positions of the arm are shown in Fig. 5. In the initial position *OB* the arm makes the same angle ($\psi_0 = 65°$) with the shaft as that maintained throughout the first stage. As the hands sweep down to the impact position C the angle ψ steadily increases until arm and shaft are in line at impact.

A comparison of Fig. 5 with the Jones multi-flash picture at any equal number of 0·01 sec intervals from the impact position shows the position of hands and club to be almost identical in the two cases. The agreement is certainly good enough to warrant the conclusion that the forces that produced the motion depicted in Fig. 5 must be very close to those that Bobby Jones actually exerted when the multi-flash photograph was taken. These forces are considered next.

Forces applied by the hands

The whole purpose of the present exercise is to find out what forces the player must have exerted and how these forces must have varied in the course of the downswing. We have already seen that the inertia forces at the clubhead are almost entirely directed *along* the shaft, those directed in a transverse direction amounting to only 1 lb during the first stage and progressively dropping in value during the second stage to practically vanish at impact. It is convenient therefore to consider the hands as applying a component force along the shaft, an almost negligible component at right angles to the shaft, and a couple equal to the latter component multiplied by the length of the shaft.

Pull along shaft:

$$F_l = -X \cos(\theta + \psi - \pi) - Y \sin(\theta + \psi - \pi). \tag{28}$$

Drag force perpendicular to shaft:

$$F_p = -X \sin(\theta + \psi - \pi) + Y \cdot \cos(\theta + \psi - \pi). \tag{29}$$

Couple:

$$C = aF_p = -Xa \sin(\theta + \psi - \pi) + Ya \cos(\theta + \psi - \pi). \tag{30}$$

The physical significance of the couple C is best recognized from the player's point of view as the trifling factor that it is by noting, not the product aF_p, but the transverse drag force F_p itself. This, as already shown, is constant throughout the first stage and thereafter (equation (12)) drops to negligible values as indicated in Fig. 5.

The component F_l of the inertia force at the clubhead is obtained by substituting in (28) the expressions for X and Y given by (3) and (4) for the first stage and by (13) for the second stage. This gives for the first stage

$$(F_l)_1 = m(a - b \cos \psi_0)\dot{\theta}^2 + mb\ddot{\theta} \sin \psi_0, \tag{31}$$

where θ^2 and $\ddot{\theta}$ are given by (10) and (11). For the second stage,

$$(F_l)_2 = ma(\omega_0 + \dot{\psi})^2 - mb\omega_0^2 \cos \psi. \tag{32}$$

The numerical values of these forces at chosen positions in the down-swing are shown in Fig. 5. They range from 20 lb at the end of the first stage to 107 lb at impact.

The corresponding values of the transverse force F_p, 1 lb and $\frac{1}{8}$ lb respectively, emphasises their insignificance.

A better physical conception of what is implied by a straight pull along the shaft is obtained by resolving the pull into two normal components, one tangential, which does all the work, and the other radial, which does no work, and is therefore merely incidental from the player's point of view.

The *tangential pull* in the first stage is given by

$$T_1 = (F_l)_1 \sin \psi_0 - P_0 \cos \psi_0, \tag{33}$$

and in the second stage by

$$T_2 = (F_l)_2 \sin \psi - P \cos \psi$$
$$= ma(\omega_0 + \dot{\psi})^2 \sin \psi - \tfrac{1}{2}mb\omega_0^2 \sin 2\psi - P \cos \psi, \tag{34}$$

where P is given by (12), in which P_0 is equal to 1 lb. T_1 and T_2 are plotted in Fig. 5 as the polar intercept between the circular arc $ABFC$ and the curve $GHKC$. According to the scale used, GA, BH and FK represent pulls of 2 lb, 20 lb, and 70 lb respectively.

The *radial tension force* in the arm in the first stage is given by

$$R_1 = -(F_l)_1 \cos \psi_0 - P_0 \sin \psi_0, \tag{35}$$

and in the second stage by

$$R_2 = -(F_l)_2 \cos \psi - P \sin \psi$$
$$= -ma \cos \psi(\omega_0 + \dot{\psi})^2 + mb\omega_0^2 \cos^2\psi - P \sin \psi. \tag{36}$$

On inserting the numerical values adopted earlier, we find that the pull R exerted by the arm is negative throughout the first stage and varies from 0·9 lb at the start to 10 lb at the end. In the second stage the negative pull drops in value to $-0·6$ lb at $\psi = 90°$, immediately after which it changes sign to increase rapidly as shown in the following table.

TABLE 1

ψ	65·0° (= ψ_0)	90°	120°	150°	180°
R_2 (lb)	-10	$-0·6$	40	86	107

As already mentioned, the pull in the arm does no work and is of only incidental interest to the player.

Work done during the downswing

The kinetic energy gained by the clubhead must equal the work done, and a useful check on the analysis is obtained by comparing the two. The work done is given by

$$W = b \int_{\theta=0}^{2\cdot89} T \, d\theta, \tag{37}$$

where T is the tangential pull of the hands as given by the polar diagram of Fig. 5. This works out at 220 ft lb, which agrees with the kinetic energy.

Velocity of equivalent clubhead

It is interesting to see how the velocity of the equivalent clubhead varies with time during the two stages of the downswing. The curve of velocity against time is shown in Fig. 6. Here OA refers to the rigid-body first stage of the motion and BC refers to the second stage. The

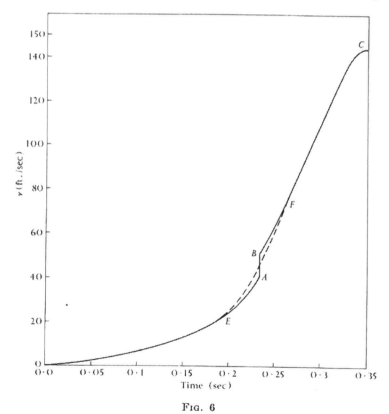

Fig. 6

impulsive change of velocity at the transition between the two stages previously discussed is represented by AB. Also as pointed out before, the actual transition occurs at some point E and the true curve bridges the discontinuity AB by taking the dotted line path EF.

Acceleration of equivalent clubhead

The acceleration of the equivalent clubhead is best visualized by reference to the velocity curve of Fig. 6. It is seen from this that the acceleration starts at about 50 ft/sec², gradually increases to about 800 ft/sec² at the end of the first stage, and then reaches 1000 ft/sec² early in the second stage, thereafter remaining constant for nearly the whole of the second stage, at the end of which it drops quickly to zero. This nearly constant acceleration of the clubhead during the second stage is in marked contrast to the tangential force applied by the hands shown in the polar diagram of Fig. 5.

5. Discussion of results obtained

The most important point to emerge from the present analytical approach is that, by making use of no more than the basic facts disclosed by the Bobby Jones multi-flash photograph, it has been possible to deduce in detail the forces that must have been applied to produce that photographic record. The truth of this rests on the fact that the successive positions of hands and club shown in Fig. 5 and in the Jones photograph are practically identical at identical times.

With this point established, one can with some confidence turn to the various interesting results that are disclosed by the analysis.

(i) Moment (or leverage) applied by the hands

The idea that the muscular action entailed in straightening, or uncocking the wrists as the hands approach the impact position (i.e. as the club moves from position FH to position CG in Fig. 5) is a major factor in increasing clubhead velocity has been shown to be a fallacy. The fallacy clearly arises from a 'post-hoc-ergo-propter-hoc' kind of reasoning.

(ii) Successive positions of clubshaft as affected by clubhead velocity at impact

If we assume that Bobby Jones' swing, as recorded in the multi-flash photograph, can be taken as representing an ideal swing, it follows that the pattern of successive positions taken up by the clubshaft establishes an ideal sequence for gaining clubhead speed in the most efficient way.

Since only inertia forces are concerned, any change in the tempo of the swing (by quickening or slowing down the whole process) produces no change in the pattern of successive positions of hands and club but only a change in the applied force. Thus, if a film of Jones' swing were run at r times the speed it was taken at, one would see a real-life swing in which the applied force is r^2 times the force used by Jones. The truth of this, of course follows from elementary first principles and is independent of the present analysis. It is, however, of great importance, for it shows that no player need fail from lack of strength to copy Jones' swing in every detail except the tempo at which it is carried out. Because the pattern of successive positions need not change, whatever the physical strength of the player, such characteristics of a first-class swing as late-hitting (as it is called) is not, as popularly supposed, confined to the strong athletic type of player. In brief, whatever may be the pattern of the ideal swing, failure to follow it is not to be attributed to lack of muscular strength, for muscular strength determines only the time-rate at which it is performed and therefore the clubhead speed and the distance the ball travels (since that distance has been shown (2) to be directly proportional to clubhead speed).

(iii) *Relative contributions of ω_0 and $\dot{\psi}$ to clubhead velocity at impact*

It is interesting to note the relative contributions of the angular velocity ω_0 of the hands (i.e. of the arm OA about the centre of rotation O in Fig. 5) and that of the clubshaft $\dot{\psi}$ relative to the arm. In Fig. 5, if the shaft were a weightless in-line extension of the arm, and thus had no angular velocity relative to the arm, the velocity of the clubhead at impact would be

$$(1 \cdot 2a + b)\omega_0 = (3 \cdot 3 + 2 \cdot 2)15 \cdot 5 = 85 \text{ ft/sec.} \tag{38}$$

The fact that CL has an angular velocity $\dot{\psi}$ relative to OC increases the velocity of the clubhead by

$$(1 \cdot 2a)\dot{\psi} = 3 \cdot 3 \times 24 \cdot 5 = 80 \text{ ft/sec.} \tag{39}$$

Thus, nearly half the clubhead velocity derives from the sweep of the clubhead past the line of the arm. Any action that interferes with the free hinge-like movement of the wrists is therefore likely to reduce the $\dot{\psi}$ contribution to the clubhead velocity. A heaving action of the body, in which the wrists stiffen at impact and so tend to keep the shaft in line with the arm after impact, may thus be a potent cause of loss of distance.

(iv) *Importance of correctly timing the applied moment during the first stage*

Equation (9) shows that in the first stage of the swing the two large inertia forces $mr\ddot{\theta}$ and $mr\dot{\theta}^2$ must be nicely balanced if the resultant of their components normal to the shaft is to be equal to the relatively small constant value P_0 of 1 lb. The player has direct control over the moment $mr\ddot{\theta}$ but only indirect control of the centrifugal force $mr\dot{\theta}^2$ through the moment $P_0 a$ fed back (so to speak) to his wrists. He must therefore generate such an angular acceleration $\ddot{\theta}$ as to limit the inertia force P_0 transverse to the shaft to a value that is quite small (only about 1 lb in Bobby Jones' swing). In Bobby Jones' swing the way in which $\ddot{\theta}$ varies during the first stage is shown by the curve DEF in Fig. 3.

This curve is of the utmost significance. It is a direct measure of the muscular effort applied by the player in the first stage and shows how very gentle the initial physical effort must be if the right conditions for starting the second stage of the swing are to be established. Achieving this gentle start is about the most difficult task that the learner has to face because he has resolutely to curb his natural instinct to apply his maximum muscular effort without delay. Such application implies a constant angular acceleration which, for the same terminal angular velocity ω_0, is represented by the straight line FG.

It is instructive to find that, if the club is swung with this constant acceleration *while maintaining ψ_0 constant*, the transverse force at the clubhead is 4·3 lb at the start, zero at a θ of 0·44 rad, when it changes sign to reach $(-4\cdot2)$ lb at the end of the stage. No player could maintain a constant wrist-cock angle under such conditions. What is likely to happen half-way through the first stage, when the heavy initial cocking force has disappeared and an equally heavy uncocking force is taking over, is that the player fails to resist the sudden change, gives way to the uncocking force and so allows the second stage to begin when the angular velocity $\dot{\theta}$ is less than half what it ought to be. The swing, in other words, is ruined by what golfers call 'hitting from the tap.'

(v) *Relation between the first and second stages of the downswing*

As already pointed out, if the tempo of the first stage is changed, that of the second stage as defined by ω_0 must be changed in the same ratio if the correct pattern of successive positions of hands and club is to be preserved. Because of the comparatively small effort in the first stage required to reach such angular velocity ω_0 as demands the player's maximum effort to maintain throughout the second stage, it is very easy for the player to overreach himself by attaining a velocity ω_0 that he is unable to keep up in the second stage. The result of such overreaching is that the hands have to slow down, with the inevitable consequence of too-early uncocking of the wrists and loss of clubhead speed.

The success of the whole swing is thus doubly sensitive to the way in which the first stage is carried out. In the first place, the terminal velocity ω_0, whatever its value, must be reached by an acceleration $\ddot{\theta}$ that varies with time in the way shown by curve DEF of Fig. 2. In the second place the value of ω_0 must be just right for the particular player. In other words, it must be large enough to enable him to exploit his full strength in the subsequent second stage, but no larger. If, at the end of the first stage, he has reached the (for him) correct ω_0 while the force P is still positive and small, there is little chance of going wrong in the second stage, always with the proviso that the wrists maintain their hinge-like action at impact.

REFERENCES

1. OSCAR FRALEN, *Golf in Action* (A. A. Wyn Inc., New York, 1952).
2. D. WILLIAMS, *Q. Jl. Mech. appl. Math.* **12** (1959) 387.

DRAG FORCE ON A GOLF BALL IN FLIGHT AND ITS PRACTICAL SIGNIFICANCE

By D. WILLIAMS (*Royal Aircraft Establishment, Farnborough*)

[Received 25 April 1958]

SUMMARY

An experimental method of measuring the aerodynamic drag of a golf ball in free flight under typical playing conditions is described and the results obtained are discussed. The method depends on deriving a curve in which the 'carry' of the ball is plotted against initial ball velocity off the tee, so that only these two parameters need to be measured. A main conclusion is that the variation of the drag coefficient with Reynolds number is such as to make the drag vary linearly rather than as the square of the velocity (over the relevant speeds), with a consequent advantage to long hitters.

1. Introduction

THE forces acting on a golf ball in flight have been the subject of a number of investigations in the past. Of these probably the latest is that carried out by J. M. Davies (1) in 1949. Apart from presenting a comprehensive review of previous work, he describes in his paper a number of experiments carried out in the small wind tunnel of the B. F. Goodrich Co. The effect of various degrees of surface smoothness and of rotational velocity on the lift and drag of the ball were measured and some interesting results were obtained. Unfortunately, however, all the experiments were made at a constant tunnel speed of 105 ft/sec and therefore at a constant Reynolds number of 88,000. It was therefore not possible to estimate how the aerodynamic forces on the ball vary with the higher Reynolds numbers achieved in practice.

It is true, of course, that a fair amount of data on the drag of spheres of varying degrees of roughness over a wide range of Reynolds number already exists and is recorded in the standard textbooks. It is all based, however, on wind-tunnel tests on non-rotating spheres with a type of surface roughness very different from that of the conventional dimpled golf ball. But, although it would be hazardous to use this data for estimating the forces on a golf ball in free flight, it has amply demonstrated the interesting fact—and particularly interesting from the golfer's point of view—of the sudden and very marked drop in the drag coefficient at a certain critical Reynolds number.

It is now well known that this drop is due to the fact that the transition from laminar to turbulent flow occurs earlier in the passage of the air over the ball, thereby narrowing the wake and reducing the drag.

Past experimental work has also shown that the smoother the surface of the sphere the more sudden the drop in the drag coefficient, and that, beyond a certain degree of roughness, the drop starts at a much lower speed and is distributed over a much wider speed range. Again it is difficult to translate the results of experiments on non-rotating spheres with particular types of roughness, in tunnels of a particular degree of turbulence, in terms of the spinning golf ball in free flight with its own peculiar type of surface roughness.

The ordinary handicap golfer's interest in this problem arises from his suspicion that the long drives achieved by the professional player are largely due to some peculiarity in the behaviour of the ball which he himself is unable to exploit but which he feels is 'just round the corner' if only he could achieve that little extra initial velocity. The matter is also of interest to the ruling body that governs the game, for if it were found that there is a critical speed which, if reached, gives the player something for nothing, so to speak, some action might be taken to obviate what might be considered an unfair advantage.

It was with such considerations in mind that the writer evolved a fairly reliable method of determining how the drag of a golf ball varies with its speed under typical playing conditions. To make the conditions typical, the ball must be struck by a lofted club-head similar to that of a driver so that, with typical back-spin, it follows the orthodox flight path of a good drive.

Two parameters alone need be measured—the initial velocity of the ball and its 'carry', i.e. the distance it covers before striking the ground. By plotting the 'carry' against the initial velocity a curve is obtained the tangent to which at any particular initial velocity gives the aerodynamic drag at that velocity.

It is claimed that this is not a 'rough-and-ready' method of obtaining the drag coefficient of a golf ball under typical playing conditions but a perfectly sound method that leads to results that are inaccurate only in so far as the two relevant parameters are inaccurately measured. This is the only reason for the use of the phrase 'fairly reliable'.

The necessary tests, which covered a range of carry extending from 150 to 230 yd, were carried out by Messrs. Dunlops (through the courtesy of Mr. S. G. Ball), and the data they obtained is plotted in Fig. 1. From this it is seen that, between the chosen limits of initial velocity, the curve is well represented by a straight line, so that the tangent to the curve is constant.

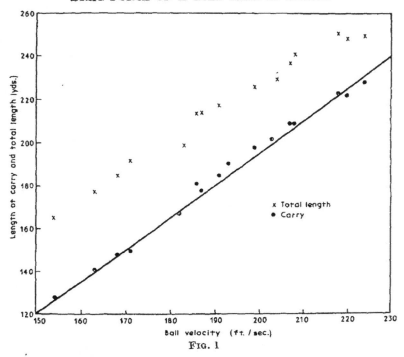

FIG. 1

2. The theoretical basis

Fig. 2 shows the trajectory for a typical drive, in which the initial angle α of the flight path is very shallow and its final angle β, where it meets the ground is fairly steep.

Let x_0 be the total carry, v the ball velocity, and v_0 the initial velocity of ball.

Consider the trajectory AB for which the initial velocity is v_0 and the total carry x_0. Suppose now the ball is teed up at A' a very short distance $\delta_1 x_0$ behind A and slightly below it by an amount $\delta_1 x_0 \tan \alpha$. If, starting from A', the ball is given an added velocity δv_0 that sends it along precisely the same path AHB as before, it will reach a point B' on the same level as A' and beyond B by the distance BC', where

$$BC' = \delta_2 x_0 = B'C' \cot \beta = \delta_1 x_0 \tan \alpha \cot \beta. \tag{1}$$

The total carry on the level is thus

$$A'B' = (x_0 + \delta x_0) = (x_0 + \delta_1 x_0 + \delta_2 x_0) \tag{2}$$

and the increase in carry is

$$\delta x_0 = \delta_1 x_0 + \delta_2 x_0 = \delta_1 x_0 (1 + \tan \alpha \cot \beta). \tag{3}$$

Since, in order to follow the same trajectory, the velocity v_0 at A must be the same in both cases, the velocity $(v_0+\delta v_0)$ at A' must have dropped by the amount δv_0 in its passage from A' to A. We can therefore write

$$\frac{\delta v_0}{\delta_1 x_0} = -\frac{\delta v}{\delta x} \qquad (4)$$

or, by (3), and introducing differentials,

$$(1+\tan\alpha\cot\beta)\frac{dv_0}{dx_0} = -\frac{dv}{dx}. \qquad (5)$$

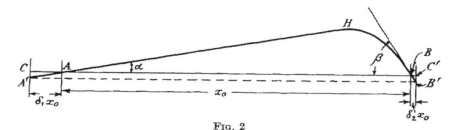

Fig. 2

Now α is normally about $6°$ and β about $45°$, which makes

$$(1+\tan\alpha\cot\beta) = 1\cdot105, \qquad (6)$$

and it is clear that small errors in α or β are of minor importance.

Reverting now to the experimental results of Fig. 1, we see that the constant slope as measured is

$$dx_0/dv_0 = 120\times3/80 = 4\cdot5 \text{ sec}, \qquad (7)$$

and therefore, by (5) and (6),

$$(dv/dx)_{v=v_0} = -(dv_0/dx_0)_{\text{measured}}\times1\cdot105 = -\frac{1\cdot105}{4\cdot5} = -0\cdot246 \text{ sec}^{-1}. \qquad (8)$$

The equation of motion of the ball in its line of travel as it leaves the tee (if we neglect gravity and the lift due to the spin, both negligible at this stage and also tending to cancel each other) takes the form

$$mv\frac{dv}{dx}\cos\alpha+Kv^2 = 0 \qquad (9)$$

or, with sufficient accuracy, since $\cos\alpha\sim1$

$$\frac{dv}{dx}+\frac{Kv}{m} = 0. \qquad (10)$$

Here v = velocity of ball in ft/sec,

m = mass of ball of weight $1 \cdot 62$ oz = $(1 \cdot 62/16)/g$ slugs ($g = 32 \cdot 2$),

$K = \frac{1}{2}C_D \rho S = 17 \times 10^{-6} C_D$,

C_D = aerodynamic drag coefficient,

S = projected area of ball = $\frac{1}{4}\pi d^2 = 0 \cdot 0143$ ft²,

d = diameter of ball = $1 \cdot 62/12$ ft,

ρ = mass of air per cu ft = $0 \cdot 00237$ slugs (at sea-level).

Inserting the appropriate numerical constants in (10) we obtain the relation

$$\frac{1}{v}\left(\frac{dv}{dx}\right) = -0 \cdot 00536 C_D \tag{11}$$

or, from (8)

$$C_D = \frac{0 \cdot 246}{(0 \cdot 00536)v} = \frac{46 \cdot 0}{v}. \tag{12}$$

Thus, for ball velocities ranging from 150 ft/sec to 230 ft/sec, which represents the practical range, the drag coefficient varies inversely with the velocity. The total drag therefore increases only linearly with the velocity instead of as the velocity squared, as it would for a constant drag coefficient. The penalty suffered by the hard hitter is therefore substantially reduced.

Using the value of C_D given by (12) in the expression for K, we obtain the total drag on the ball as

$$(17 \times 10^{-6})C_D v^2 \text{ lb} = 0 \cdot 000783v \text{ lb}. \tag{13}$$

Thus at the initial velocity of 190 ft/sec, which gives a carry of 180 yd— a typical distance for the average player—the drag coefficient from formula (12) has the value $0 \cdot 242$. For a long drive of 232 yd carry the initial velocity is 225 ft/sec at which the drag coefficient is $0 \cdot 204$, a reduction of 16 per cent.

It is of interest to see how much of the difference in length between the long hitter and the average player is due to this drop in the drag coefficient. To determine this we use the numerical values just quoted and suppose that the drag coefficient for speeds between 190 ft/sec and 225 ft/sec remains constant at $0 \cdot 242$—the value appropriate to 190 ft/sec. From (11), on putting $0 \cdot 242$ for C_D, we have

$$\frac{1}{v}\frac{dv}{dx} = -0 \cdot 00536 C_D = -0 \cdot 0013 \tag{11}$$

for which the solution is

$$\log_e v = -0 \cdot 0013x + \text{constant}.$$

Using the condition that $v = v_0$ when $x = 0$, we write

$$\log_e v/v_0 = -0\cdot0013x.$$

The distance travelled while the velocity drops from v_0 ($= 225$ ft/sec) to v_1 ($= 190$ ft/sec) is therefore

$$x = \left(\frac{1}{0\cdot0013}\right)\log_e \frac{225}{190} = 129 \text{ ft} = 43 \text{ yd.} \tag{14}$$

Comparing this with the actual distance of $(232-180) = 52$ yd, we see that the long hitter gains just over 9 yd. It can be said therefore that only some 17 per cent of the long hitter's advantage in distance can be attributed to the drop in drag coefficient. The rest apparently he gains by honest effort.

REFERENCE

1. J. M. DAVIES, 'The aerodynamics of golf balls', *J. Appl. Phys.* **20** (1949) 821–8.

DR DAVID WILLIAMS

Dr David Williams, a graduate of the University of Wales, a Doctor of Science, a Fellow of the Institute of Mechanical Engineers, a Fellow of the Royal Aeronautical Society and a Chartered Engineer, made his career in the Scientific Civil Service and was a Deputy Chief Scientific Officer (Special Merit) at the Royal Aircraft Establishment, Farnborough - an appointment made only for outstanding individual research. He was internationally recognised as a leading aeronautical research engineer and has a large number of scientific papers to his name, including a textbook on the *Theory of Aircraft Structures*. He was a Structures and Dynamics Consultant and a member of the Structures Committee of the Aeronautical Research Council. The Sims Gold Medal and the Society's Bronze Medal, awarded by the Royal Aeronautical Society bear evidence of the Society's recognition of his work.

His interest in dynamical problems led him into fields outside aeronautics, as witness his paper on 'The Drag of Golf Balls in Flight' and his prize-winning paper on 'The Mathematical Theory of the Snaking of Caravans' read to the Institution of Mechanical Engineers - the first ever to explain that bothersome phenomenon. After retirement he became a Dynamics consultant to the Research Department of British Rail where he was concerned with the structural and dynamical problems raised by the projected 150 m.p.h. light passenger train.

Such is the background against which his scientific paper on the *Dynamics of the Golf Swing* (May 1967) - the basis of the present book - was written.

Made in the USA
Las Vegas, NV
06 August 2023

75700602R00092